The
Armand Hammer
Collection

Five Centuries of Masterpieces

The Armand Hammer Foundation makes possible exchanges of art, sponsors medical research and promotes international understanding for the progress of people everywhere.

This exhibition is made possible by The Armand Hammer Foundation

Photography by Seth Joel

Printed by
Southern California Graphics
Los Angeles, California

Library of Congress Cataloging in Publication Data

Armand Hammer Foundation.
    The Armand Hammer Collection.

    "This catalogue represents the Armand Hammer Collect-
    ion as it exists in April 1981"—Acknowledgements.
    1. Painting—Exhibitions. 2. Hammer, Armand,
    1897-   —Art collections—Exhibitions. I. Title.
    N5220.H26A75 1981   750'.74   81-2042
                                        AACR2

Cover
Rembrandt van Rijn 1606-1669
Juno, detail
Oil on canvas 127.0 x 122.87 cm.

Contents

5   Foreword   Armand Hammer

6   Preface   Kenneth Donahue

7   Acknowledgments   Dennis Gould, Quinton Hallett

8   Introduction   John Walker

17   Armand Hammer Collection Exhibitions

19   Paintings

163   Drawings, Pastels and Watercolors

275   Index

Armand Hammer

Photograph: Tom Atkinson

Foreword

The artists who created these paintings and drawings have provided us with a legacy that must be preserved and shared. Preservation and sharing is a responsibility of enlightened collectors. It is a task and I eagerly accept because the joy and satisfaction it brings me is more rewarding than the mere possession of art.

The enjoyment of art should not be limited to the fortunate few who collect. Instead, the works of artistic genius should be available to all. That is why this collection constantly travels from city to city and nation to nation. This collection is especially for those who are unable to travel extensively to view works of art in the world's great museums. This collection is not for the few—it is for people everywhere.

There is no language barrier to these works of art. People who see this collection are moved and inspired by it wherever it is shown. To me this international response is a reaffirmation that all the people on earth are joined more by hopes and dreams than they are divided by differences.

As this exhibition continues to travel, it will remain an emissary creating better understanding between nations. Through this understanding we can expect that the wonder and delight in the world captured by these artists will be enjoyed in an era of peace and prosperity for all.

Armand Hammer

Preface

Dr. Armand Hammer is a world citizen in his business life, a world resident in his private life. His philosophy of art and his sense of trusteeship as a collector are equally international in perspective. "A drawing by Rembrandt or a painting by van Gogh doesn't communicate only in Dutch," Dr. Hammer observes, "it speaks in English, French, Spanish, Russian, Japanese, and in as many other languages as there are viewers." For him, the work of art transcends not only linguistic barriers but the limits of language itself in expressing many subtleties of human experience and human perception which cannot be formulated in words. It is, therefore, an ideal vehicle not only for giving visual pleasures to people wherever they might live but also for expanding their understanding of man both individually, as a feeling and thinking being and commonly, as part of the diverse social and cultural complexes he has created.

The collection that Dr. Hammer assembled is one of considerable variety, extending from the Renaissance into the first decades of the 20th century, having as its unifying constituent the representation of man and nature. It includes works of artists like Rembrandt and van Gogh who were deeply concerned with the human condition and psychology. French realists and American artists who recorded their personal visions of nature are also represented. Others who extracted elements from nature to be savored aesthetically are included: color for the Impressionists, form for Cézanne and Seurat.

In keeping with his belief in the importance of works of art as vehicles of pleasure and understanding, Dr. Hammer has a deeply felt commitment to sharing his collection. Consequently, no other private collection has been seen in recent times by so many people in such different parts of the world — literally more than three million persons during the past decade. In the same spirit, the catalogue has been translated into Russian, Japanese, Swedish, Spanish and French.

Echoing the museum directors of Europe, Asia, North America and South America, who have had the privilege of exhibiting the Hammer collection, I would like to express special appreciation to Dr. and Mrs. Armand Hammer for giving such rich experiences and so much joy to the people we serve.

Kenneth Donahue
Director Emeritus
Los Angeles County Museum of Art

Acknowledgments

The Armand Hammer Collection has a remarkable impact on three main levels of understanding. First, to scholars and students of art history, the collection presents some of the world's most influential artists working in a range of media over a period of several centuries. Accessibility to the collection provides opportunities for study and increasing connoisseurship of these artists. Second, the timeless quality inherent in the works transcends political difficulties between nations, rendering the collection an international emissary of peace as it travels to cities throughout the world. Third and most important, the collection is able to enrich the lives of millions as it travels close to people who might never otherwise have a chance to see such a repository of treasures.

This catalogue represents the Armand Hammer Collection as it exists in April 1981. It has grown along with the collection, and it reflects the contributions of many individuals who prepared the original entries or who have provided notes on the most recent acquisitions.

Most of the original entries were prepared by the staff of the Los Angeles County Museum of Art. To this original group, others have willingly added their expertise. For specific catalogue entries we would like to thank: Adelyn D. Breeskin, curator emerita and consultant, Department of 20th Century Painting and Sculpture, National Collection of Fine Arts (now renamed the National Museum of American Art); J. Fred Cain, Jr., former curator, National Gallery of Art, Washington, D.C.; Larry J. Curry, former fellow, National Gallery of Art, Washington, D.C.; Kenneth Donahue, director emeritus, Los Angeles County Museum of Art; Marcia Early, former fellow, National Gallery of Art, Washington, D.C.; Ebria Feinblatt, senior curator, Prints and Drawings, Los Angeles County Museum of Art; Dr. Harold McCracken, director emeritus, Buffalo Bill Historical Center, Cody, Wyoming; Charles Millard, chief curator, Hirshhorn Museum and Sculpture Garden, Washington, D.C.; Konrad Oberhuber, curator of drawings, professor of fine arts, Fogg Art Museum, Harvard University, Cambridge, Massachusetts; Seymore Slive, director, Fogg Art Museum, Harvard University, Cambridge, Massachusetts; John Walker, director emeritus, National Gallery of Art, Washington, D.C.; Christopher White, director, Centre for Studies in British Art, London. (Initials of individuals who provided the documentation appear at the end of each entry.) John Walker and Kenneth Donahue deserve special acknowledgment for their contributions to this catalogue and for documentation of the Armand Hammer Collection. They continue to offer sound advice and to participate in a project that has involved them for years. We would also like to thank Carolyn H. Wells, research assistant to John Walker, for her review of earlier Hammer catalogues and Martha Wade Kaufman, former curator of the Armand Hammer Collection and director of art of the Armand Hammer Foundation, for all her work on behalf of the collection and previous catalogues.

We are indebted to several others who were directly responsible for the realization of this catalogue: Ruth W. Spiegel for editing divergent sources into a uniform text; Seth Joel for his photography of the entire collection; Warren Kennaugh for catalogue design; and Sheri Hirst for supervision of the catalogue production. Ultimately, the man who deserves the highest credit for sharing his treasures with the world is Dr. Armand Hammer. Without his deep personal concern for peace through international understanding, exhibitions and catalogues of this kind would not be possible.

Dennis A. Gould
Director
The Armand Hammer Foundation

Quinton Hallett
Assistant Director
The Armand Hammer Foundation

Introduction

I once asked Armand Hammer why he collected. "Because it's fun!" he explained. "It's a hunt. I get a certain joy out of finding rare works, out of learning the stories attached to them. I've always liked to collect. I used to collect stamps. My father had a great stamp collection. But pictures are something more than just collecting. You are connecting yourself with something that really is immortal, something that has survived all these centuries. You are preserving something for posterity."

Armand Hammer is a doctor of medicine, although he has never practiced. He received his degree from the Columbia University College of Physicians and Surgeons, studying at night and in the daytime running a family pharmaceutical company. His father, Julius, was a doctor and was struggling to keep the tiny family firm from bankruptcy. Armand took over and made it so profitable that upon graduation he had a clear profit of one million dollars.

While waiting to begin his internship at the Bellevue Medical Center, Armand (grandson of a Russian emigrant) decided, in 1921, to go to Russia to help combat a typhus epidemic that was raging in the Urals. He set off, equipped with medical knowledge and a field hospital he had purchased. When he reached the Russian interior, after many difficulties, he found that starvation, not typhus, was the real enemy. The famine he saw struck him, as he said, "with cold horror." He decided to use a substantial part of his capital to eliminate the terrible shortage of food. He entered into an agreement with the local Soviet that he buy a million bushels of American wheat, which he estimated would feed the people until next year's crop could be harvested. He stipulated, however, that the ships bringing the grain be filled with Russian goods which could be sold in the United States, so that the food supply could be replenished.

When Lenin heard of this, he asked to meet this young American, who at age twenty-three had become a hero in the Urals. The meeting between the two was an immediate success. They became and remained firm friends. Lenin proposed that Armand Hammer accept one or more Soviet concessions. After thinking over the offer, he decided to choose two: one for mining asbestos, which proved minimally profitable, and a second for an export-import business, which succeeded beyond his most sanguine hopes. He eventually represented thirty-seven leading American companies; and he was the first to import Fordson tractors, thus beginning the mechanization of Russian agriculture.

He settled down in Moscow and spent the next nine years in the Soviet Union. Needing a residence, he rented an unfurnished palace and decorating it gave him his first interest in art. His younger brother, Victor, who had studied art history at Princeton, became Armand's tutor. Together they bought, for next to nothing, eighteenth century French furniture, Aubusson rugs, services of Sèvres china, Meissen porcelains, Fabergé objects — all the household furnishings brought into Commission Stores by the impoverished aristocracy and even the middle class.

Around 1928, a New York art dealer, seeing the bargains the Hammer brothers were picking up, offered them a partnership in his firm. Armand soon bought out the other partner, who had been ruined in the stock market collapse and the Hammer Galleries were established. Meanwhile, the Hammer palace in Moscow rivalled any museum of decorative arts and overflowed into several warehouses. Having paid a tax to the Soviets, the brothers were allowed to export these treasures; and this became the stock which Armand and Victor brilliantly sold in the Hammer Galleries over a period of years. This, the first Hammer collection, has all been dispersed. It was essentially a way of converting rubles into dollars.

Thus, for a long time art dealing has been the avocation of Armand Hammer. He is the president of Hammer Galleries as well as president of M. Knoedler and Co., Inc. Victor is the active manager of the Hammer Galleries. But Armand's real vocation has been searching for still more rewarding enterprises.

In Russia, apart from his export-import business, he built and operated a pencil factory, which at its peak, produced seventy-two million pencils and ninety-five million pens a year and made a tremendous profit. After departing from Russia in 1930, he ran a private bank in Paris which specialized in discounting Soviet notes at twenty-four percent per annum. The notes were held until they were paid in full, often yielding as much as seventy percent on each transaction. He then returned to America and, after having sold most of his Russian collection, helped liquidate the Hearst works of art.

During World War II he built the first distillery in America to make alcohol from potatoes and substituting potato spirits for embargoed grain spirits, he developed a valuable business in blended whiskey. After the war he bought several other distilleries that used the more conventional grain alcohol. In a few years he built the J. W. Dant brand from a relatively unknown Kentucky bourbon into a company selling over a million cases a year. In 1954 he sold this whiskey empire to Schenley Distillers and moved to California. But Armand Hammer's most successful venture was his investment in Occidental Petroleum Corporation, of which he has been president and is now chairman and chief executive officer. To give some idea of the growth of this company under his leadership, in 1956, when he first became associated with it, its net worth was thirty-four thousand dollars; today its net worth is more than one billion dollars.

Occidental Petroleum has made possible the third Hammer collection. There was a second Hammer collection, formed in the fifties and given to the University of Southern California in 1965. Those paintings constitute an important group of Old Masters, intended for study purposes, and have proved invaluable in a university museum. But after he had given them away, Dr. Hammer began a more ambitious collection, with a particular emphasis on French Impressionists, Post-Impressionists, and Old Master paintings and drawings. This, the third Hammer collection, is illustrated and annotated in the present catalogue. Today this exceptional group of paintings and drawings, that spans over five centuries, contains more than one hundred Western European and American masterpieces, including works by Leonardo da Vinci, Michelangelo, Picasso and Chagall.

The uniqueness and quality of these valuable art works are evident in the paintings of the period extending from the sixteenth to the twentieth century. The "crown jewel" of the collection is the *Juno* by Rembrandt, once owned by William Middendorf. I recall how, when I first saw it exhibited, this supremely beautiful work struck me as unsurpassed among its greatest peers. It is, in my opinion, the finest single work of art which has remained in an American private collection. Like the drawing by Leonardo, it too is a memory image — a loving tribute to Hendrickje Stoffels, Rembrandt's mistress, who died in 1663, probably the year the canvas was begun. Dr. Hammer has said that he acquired the painting with the intention of presenting it to the Los Angeles County Museum of Art. In the rapidly growing collection of that remarkable gallery, the Rembrandt *Juno* will long remain its outstanding treasure and a magnet for visitors to the museum.

Though the focus is on paintings of the nineteenth and twentieth centuries, the works of several earlier masters are represented. The Los Angeles County Museum of Art was able, through the Frances and Armand Hammer Purchase Fund, to acquire two splendid seventeenth century panels: Rembrandt's *Portrait of a Man of the Raman Family* and Rubens' *The Israelites Gathering Manna in the Desert*. A second Rubens in the Hammer collection, *Young Woman with Curly Hair,* is particularly distinguished for its flesh tones as beautiful as any I know in painting — and for its modeling — breathtaking in the subtlety of the transitions of shadow.

There are only two eighteenth century paintings in the collection. The first, Fragonard's *The Education of the Virgin,* owes its chiaroscuro and sepia tones to Rembrandt and its fluent brushwork and virtuosity to Rubens. Dr. Hammer was fortunate enough to acquire for the collection the preliminary sketch for this beautiful painting. The second, a sketch by Goya for the Prado cartoon, *El Pelele,* was selected by the Spanish Society of the Friends of Art for their exhibition of Goya's work in Madrid (a fact worth noting since only the finest Spanish pictures meet their exacting standards).

Corot has always been, for Armand Hammer, a favorite artist. At one time there were twenty-four of his paintings in the collection. Of these only the six finest are being shown. Historically, the most interesting is a landscape known as *Pleasures of Evening,* an appropriate title, for it is one of the artist's last canvases. Writing about it in 1892, Jules Antoine Castagnary touchingly said, "When the imagination is still so fresh, and sensitivity still so alive, death should take pity and not interrupt." The painting has darkened with time, as often happens with Corot's late work. Thus, there will always be those who prefer the fresh, spring-like tones of *Distant View of Mantes Cathedral.* For my part, I would choose the dramatic *Medieval Ruins,* or, among figure pictures, the portrait of a young minx, *Portrait of a Girl,* whose half-smile and appraising glance enthrall me.

With Corot as its leader, the greatest school of landscape painting the world has known — even without the geniuses of Constable and Turner — flourished in and around Paris. To realize this one need only look at Boudin, whose mastery of cloud effects is impressively demonstrated by *Sailing Ships in Port;* at Renoir, whose infectious *joie de vivre* is gloriously apparent both in *Grape Pickers at Lunch* — an enchanting peasant picnic — and in *Antibes,* which suggests a modern *Embarkation for Cythera;* and at Monet whose palette, in that masterpiece of light and air, *View of Bordighera,* seems made of ground jewels. All these paintings illustrate the reason for the popularity of the Impressionists and their circle. One of the most enchanting cityscapes ever painted, Pissarro's *Boulevard Montmartre, Mardi Gras,* which recently moved from one California collector to another — from Norton Simon to Armand Hammer — shows the quintessence of Impressionist technique. The painting vibrates with light and color, an effect only possible through the use of those quick, short brushstrokes which are the hallmark of Impressionism.

There was, of course, the reaction against the Impressionists, exemplified by Cézanne, van Gogh and Gauguin. All of these artists are well represented in the Hammer collection. The Cézanne *Boy Resting* has been frequently exhibited; the Gauguin *Bonjour M. Gauguin,* a later version of which is in Prague, has been widely reproduced; and the four van Goghs: *Garden of the Rectory at Neunen* (an early work), *The Sower* (somewhat later and obviously influenced by Millet), *Lilacs* (a still life seemingly redolent of the fragrance of lilacs), and *Hospital at Saint-Rémy* (where van Gogh was confined), are all well known. The latter, once in the Norton Simon Collection, is one of van Gogh's supreme works. Of this view of the park and the asylum he wrote, "I tried to reconstruct the thing as it might have been, simplifying and accentuating the haughty, unchanging character of the pines and cedar clumps against the blue."

American collectors have been so preoccupied with the Impressionists and their followers that there has been a tendency to overlook artists who did not belong to the movement. Among these, to me the most enthralling is Gustave Moreau, who was a direct precursor of the Surrealists. The Armand Hammer Collection has two of his masterpieces, *King David* and *Salome.* The latter had a deep effect on J. K. Huysman, and in *A Rebours* he wrote a long description of the picture in prose as glittering as the painting itself. In 1876, P. de Saint-Victor said of it: "M. Gustave Moreau's entry in the Salon far exceeds any of his previous exhibits. . . . If an opium fiend could translate his visions into reality with a goldsmith's skill, it would give some idea of this artist."

Another French artist less collected than he deserves to be is Fantin-Latour. His still lifes of flowers are often to be found in American collections, though never in a finer example than Dr. Hammer's *Peonies in a Blue and White Vase;* but his superb portraits are too rarely seen. *Portrait of Miss Edith Crowe,* is one of the most poetic examples of nineteenth century portraiture. The strongly accented light and shadow create a mood of pensive brooding, the essence of the Romantic image.

The momentum of the great French artistic movements of the nineteenth century carried creativity well into the first half of the twentieth century. The artists (especially Vuillard and Bonnard) who made Paris, in our time, the mecca for painters, are beautifully shown in the collection. It is difficult to choose among the Vuillards; they are all of such high quality. But my favorite remains *At the Seashore.* Jacques Salomon, in a recent book, perfectly expresses my response to this exquisite canvas when he says, "it is like a cry from the heart, the echo of which ravished me . . . the touch is so alive, so alert, so completely submissive to the rhythm of Vuillard's feeling."

Bonnard, too, is well represented. The early *Street Scene* evokes the loveliness of the simplest happenings of Parisian life, and the *Nude Against the Light* suggests the artist's unique combination of sensitivity and sensuality, reminding one of the nudes Titian painted at the end of his life.

The next generation, which lends such lustre to the School of Paris, is to be seen in a great portrait by Modigliani, already a part of the collection of the Los Angeles County Museum of Art; by Vlaminck's *Summer Bouquet,* equaling de Staël in its display of palette knife virtuosity; and by Derain's *Still Life with Basket, Jug and Fruit,* which is distinguished for its simplicity of composition, its elimination to essential forms, and its restricted palette.

I have kept to the last two paintings, both as insubstantial as a dream: Marie Laurencin's *Women in the Forest,* which once belonged to John Quinn, the pioneer among American collectors in his early appreciation of the School of Paris; and Chagall's *Blue Angel,* which was once in the collection of Frank Crowninshield, the able editor of *Vanity Fair,* a publication largely responsible for the American vogue of these Parisian artists.

In recent years Dr. Hammer has added a few American paintings to his collection. His earliest picture is the most famous of American icons, Gilbert Stuart's *Portrait of George Washington.* Known as the "Lewis Washington," it is more interesting than many other versions, showing the first president seated at a table with his sword resting on his arm and a glimpse of sky in the distance.

A great portrait, painted just eighty years later, is Thomas Eakins' *Sebastiano Cardinal Martinelli.* In its psychological penetration, its simplicity and dignity, its noble humanity, this may well be considered an American Rembrandt. Sylvan Schendler, writing in 1967, refers to it as "the most powerful portrait of its kind ever painted by an American."

Painted slightly earlier is a fine still life by Harnett, which has the distinction of being among the few nineteenth century American pictures ever exhibited at the Royal Academy, where it was shown in 1885 and bought by an English painter, George Richmond.

The American canvas, *On the Beach,* painted in 1916 by Maurice Prendergast, is a most original and interesting American Impressionist work. Owned by Mrs. Charles Prendergast until recently, it is a picture she parted with reluctantly, as it was always considered in the family one of her brother-in-law's greatest masterpieces.

Two Americans who lived abroad, Mary Cassatt and John Singer Sargent, are superbly represented. One painting by Sargent was bought by the Los Angeles County Museum of Art with funds provided by Dr. and Mrs. Hammer. Mary Cassatt's double portrait of *Reine Lefebvre and Margot* is, in my opinion, her finest pastel done after 1900, and the idyllic *Summertime* I consider one of her two most important landscapes.

The two portraits by Sargent, though both were painted relatively early, are totally different from each other. *Dr. Pozzi at Home,* dated 1881, is highly dramatic, as though the doctor were an actor about to go on stage. It is a masterpiece of Salon painting, sophisticated and cosmopolitan. The double portrait of *Mrs. Edward L. Davis and Her Son, Livingston Davis,* is much more sober and is more American in a straightforward, realistic way. Sargent has here recorded the essence of upper-class America, which has learned to be fashionable without learning to be chic.

I have already mentioned a few of the drawings in the Armand Hammer Collection. In recent years, this part of Dr. Hammer's collection has been greatly enriched and he has built the most important private collection of drawings and watercolors in America. Several of his finest acquisitions were made in 1970 and 1971. These include: a lovely watercolor of flowers by Albrecht Dürer; a study by Raphael for S. Maria della Pace, in Rome; and two studies by Correggio, one for the pendentive of San Giovanni Evangelista in Parma and the other for the Madonna della Scodella.

Two drawings recently added to the Hammer collection are by the two most important of all Renaissance artists: Leonardo da Vinci and Michelangelo. These studies rank with the finest examples of the graphic arts ever brought to America. The Leonardo is probably part of a large sheet, which must have been the size of the drawing of the *Virgin, Christ Child, and St. John,* at Windsor, generally dated 1478-80. The ink and paper are the same and, for the following reasons, it seems to have been done at about the same time. At the bottom of the sheet there is a bust of a young girl who looks at the spectator. She closely resembles the figure of a maiden with a unicorn in a drawing by Leonardo at Oxford. Some years ago, in an article on Leonardo's *Ginevra dei Benci,* I pointed out the similarity of the Oxford sketch and the portrait — which I date about 1480, or in exactly the same period as the Windsor sheet. Fortunately, Dr. Hammer has indicated that his drawings will go to Washington. Thus the National Gallery of Art will some day have not only Ginevra's actual portrait but what might be called a memory image of her face — a tracing of that strange beauty which haunted the master's mind in his youth, in the days just after he had gained his independence from his apprenticeship with Verrocchio.

Michelangelo's double-sided drawing in black chalk of two nude men, both leaning forward, may be, as tentatively suggested by John Gere and Nicholas Turner, the germ of the concept of his greatest of all Pietàs, the one once owned by the Rondanini family. All the contours of the figures, especially the outlines of each side of the torsos and limbs, are so sensitively related one to the other that they suggest three-dimensional forms as weighty and as solid as the marble from which the Pietà was carved. It is also believed that the figures could be studies for the figures of the Epifania cartoon.

Another discovery is a biblical subject by Rembrandt in the process of being published by Christopher White. Also recently added is a brown ink, *Study of a Beggar Man and Woman,* done about 1630, that displays Rembrandt's fascination with life in Amsterdam.

At the sale of Mrs. Jesse I. Straus' fastidiously chosen collection, Dr. Hammer bought two exquisite eighteenth century sanguines by Watteau; four virtuoso sepia wash drawings by Fragonard; a serenely beautiful pencil portrait of *Mrs. Charles Badham,* drawn by Ingres when he was in Rome; and the fascinating Degas pastel of *Jacquet,* whose staring eyes are so strangely hypnotic.

From the Norton Simon sale he acquired two Boucher drawings: one, *Venus Reclining Against a Dolphin,* which was engraved by Demarteau, and the other, *Landscape,* which was selected by Agnes Mongan for *Great Drawings of All Times.*

The drawings in Dr. Hammer's collection range from the shorthand annotation of Gauguin's immediate response to nature in his *Sketchbook* to Ingres' portrait of *Mrs. Charles Badham,* fashioned as a complete and independent work of art. Ingres' idealism based on nature is a concept of art which extends back to the Renaissance, and particularly to Raphael. It is this concept that the leaders of the major movements in nineteenth century art attacked again and again, but to which they often returned for sustenance. The drawings in the Hammer collection could, in fact, be viewed as a dialectic between Ingres and the other artists represented here who affected the transition in concept, style and subject from the art of the Old Masters to modern art.

Working for the open market without ecclesiastical or aristocratic commissions, the artists of the nineteenth century had the freedom to adhere to the precepts of the Academy or to seek independent subjects, styles and livelihoods. The result was that these creative personalities produced a series of revolutions and counter-revolutions in rapid succession, paralleling the extraordinary social and intellectual development of the century. Their unifying element was the study of the Old Masters and their respect for Ingres, whose influence persists in drawings of Manet, Degas, Renoir and Seurat.

Millet, working in the middle of the century, turned first to the landscape and the peasant and eventually to the urban poor and middle class. In the Ingres portrait, the human figure so dominates its surroundings that even the grandiose city of Rome becomes a stage set for the sitter. In the Millet pastel, the peasants are an integral part of the landscape, sharing their reality with the cart and the tree and the undulations of the land. The thick line and broad surface modulations give weight and solidity to the peasant figures but, at the same time, imbue them with a simple dignity that goes back in French tradition beyond the writings of Jean Jacques Rousseau to the nobility of the peasants in the paintings of Louis LeNain.

Possibly no group of artists who exhibited together and, consequently, received a single art historical label, are more divergent than the Impressionists. Descended from the mid-century painters of reality, the Impressionists in the 1860s and 1870s espoused the common aim of depicting nature through the color and light perceived by the eye, rather than through tangible forms recreated by the intellect. In drawing, they achieved this end by softening outlines, varying the width and intensity of strokes to suggest value gradations of color, using the spare areas of the paper to enhance the illusion of light and atmosphere, and replacing traditional linear perspective with aerial perspective. The drawings, watercolors and pastels in the Hammer collection (by Pissarro, Manet, Degas and Renoir) reveal such highly individualized perceptions of "optical reality" and such different moments in the history of Impressionism that they are best considered as works by individual Impressionist artists rather than as representatives of a unified Impressionist style.

While Millet insisted that he was completely apolitical, Camille Pissarro was an anarchist with Marxian sympathies and a strong identification with the underprivileged. Yet Pissarro's representation of peasants in the *Pea Harvest,* certainly influenced by Millet, is neither polemical nor sentimental. It is rather a reflection of the Impressionist view of the subject as an essentially pictorial element. Pissarro's particular concern for the peasants is implied in his choice of them as subjects, otherwise rare in Impressionist art. He rendered them without movement, standing or kneeling, almost immobile, as though the artist wished to record their forms silhouetted against a blank background as images of timelessness. *Montmorency Road*, drawn with the utmost restraint and delicacy, is a characteristic example of Pissarro's landscape style in the medium of pencil. Here the Impressionist artist has abstracted the generalized forms of the objects, reducing them to the basic realities of light and shade.

Edouard Manet, in his early double-sided charcoal drawing of a *Man Wearing a Cloak*, adapted the grandiose concept of the figure and the use of chiaroscuro rather than modeled volumes to suggest fluid mass.

In his book, *The Nude*, Kenneth Clark wrote that Edgar Degas "was the greatest draughtsman since the Renaissance. His subject was the figure in action, his aim to communicate most vividly the idea of movement." This statement immediately conjures up the image of one of Degas' lithe ballerinas, caught in a graceful arabesque on a brilliantly lighted stage. It applies equally to the figurative pastels of the 1880s (in the Hammer collection) when Degas had abandoned spontaneous action and conventional beauty of figure and setting. The *Laundress Carrying Linen* is a descendant of Daumier's working women, but, for Degas, without social implications. It is a "figure in action" in a Poussinesque sense, embodying the tensions created by the weight of the laundry and the counteracting torsions of the figure.

The *Theater Box* captures the kaleidoscopic movement of members of the corps-de-ballet in an instantaneous pattern and gives it permanency. Experimenting with artificial illumination, Degas shrouds a large part of the composition in darkness and shadows. The cropped silhouettes emphasize the fragmented figures on stage, caught in fleeting gestures and rapid complex movements. Painted about 1885, it heralds both Expressionism and Abstract art.

Pierre Renoir, along with Monet, the purest Impressionist of the 1870s, also experienced the crisis in that style after his trip to Italy in 1881. *Girlhood*, his pencil drawing in the Hammer collection of two seated girls seen from behind, still has something of the casualness and colorism of Impressionism. The figures are not defined by a firm sculptural line like that of Ingres, but by fragile strokes of varied width and darkness which suggest atmosphere surrounding the figures and playing over the surfaces. Yet, in this drawing, the artist self-consciously transcends purely optical vision to suggest the stability of form beneath the surface.

Discovering and recording the underlying forms and structures of that bright and sunny nature revealed by the Impressionists became the artistic preoccupation of Cézanne and the Neo-Impressionists. Cézanne spoke of making Impressionism "something solid and durable like the art of the museums." Toward this end he made studies like the one in the Hammer collection of a plaster cast of a male figure with the skin removed to reveal the muscles—a cast thought at that time to be by Michelangelo. He injected into it the kind of energy welling up from within the figure that was not likely present in the cast itself. The reverse side has been described by John Rewald as a "study" for the painting *The Artist's Father* at the National Gallery of Art in Washington, D.C. To quote Rewald: "While contemplating him, often without the model's knowledge, the painter had felt the deep-rooted links that nature or fate had established between him and this old man."

The Neo-Impressionists followed Georges Seurat, whose goal was a scientific, objective and non-individualist system for depicting the essential reality of nature. He strived to capture this quality in his carefully controlled space of the *Study after "The Models."* Despite the brevity of Seurat's career, a prodigious body of drawings celebrates his genius as a draftsman. Curiously, among the several hundred drawings assigned to his hand, only two were intended by the artist to be graphically reproduced. The present drawing derives from one of Seurat's major canvases, *The Models*, and was used for an illustration in the April 15, 1888 issue of *La Vie Moderne.* In the following year, Seurat designed a cover for *L'Homme à Femme*, a novel by the Polish writer Victor Joze. Each of these studies was drawn in pen and ink, a technique that rarely appears in Seurat's drawing oeuvre. Another atypical feature common to both is the undisguised use of outline.

Henri-Edmond Cross' *Cypresses*, with its feeling of romantic nostalgia, is clear evidence that Neo-Impressionist style and technique, in other hands, could be used as a vehicle for extra-pictorial emotional communication.

The last direct derivation from Impressionism in the Hammer collection is the delicate and poetic *Girl Putting on Her Stocking* by Pierre Bonnard, who continued working in this manner into the fifth decade of the twentieth century. The present work is one of the most freely executed of these sketches, done with great economy of line. It evokes a sense of freedom and, at the same time, a springy feeling of movement which is rather infrequent in Bonnard's generally motionless figure studies.

The Hammer collection is richest in the early drawings of the two artists, Vincent van Gogh and Paul Gauguin, who led the way from Impressionism to personal, emotional expression and laid the basis for the Expressionism of the twentieth century. The two drawings of houses by van Gogh are among his very earliest serious works, dated 1879-1880. He had made drawings from childhood and had been associated with works of art during his entire life. His three brothers were art dealers and he worked as an assistant at Goupil & Co. for seven years. It was only after his dismissal from this position and his failure as an evangelist among the poor miners in the Borinage district of Belgium that he, still living among the poor workers, decided to become an artist. It was then in early 1880 that these simple charcoal studies of houses were made. There are already hints here of that nervous line which gave such vitality to his later works.

Van Gogh quickly transferred his evangelical commiseration with the poor to drawing workmen and peasants. The drawings from 1881, *Man Polishing a Boot* and the *Old Man Carrying a Bucket*, are executed in what can be called van Gogh's first personal style—rather bulky figures, tight and angular with a rich elaboration of surface. These four drawings furnish a revealing contrast to his subsequent progress. During this period he made scores of drawings after Millet and studied for fifteen months with Anton Mauve.

Of historical importance is a sketchbook of Paul Gauguin's which has been disassembled for purposes of exhibition. Gauguin purchased the sketchbook in Rouen in 1884 and used it intermittently until 1888. It includes brief lists, shopping lists, addresses and notations that clarify events in Gauguin's life during those years. Eleven pages concern Gauguin's thoughts on art, *Notes Synthétiques*, his first written statement on art theory, as well as notes on literature and music. The remaining 105 pages are filled with 268 sketches of many of the images used in pictures of the same period: landscapes, houses, animals and people, mostly from Brittany. The color crayon drawings of the *Breton Boy*, typical of Gauguin's style in the sketchbook, show that at that time the artist was still closely linked to Impressionism. The poses are informal, casual with few details. The forms dissolve in transparent etchings of light tones while other drawings clearly anticipate the arbitrary flat pattern and calligraphic line of the *Landscape at Pont-Aven,* or the primitive simplification of *Parau No Te Varau Inro,* which characterizes the later Gauguin. The *Breton Sketchbook,* Dr. Hammer has said, "is for me like being taken into the mind of the artist. It is the extension of the artist as he responds to life and records it. These drawings give insight to the creative processes."

Talking to Armand Hammer, one feels the intense intellectual concentration which enables him to develop solutions for problems and issues confronting him. In his youth it involved a pharmaceutical company and Russian famine; later the sale of Fordson tractors and the manufacture of lead pencils; after his Russian sojourn, it involved the dispersal of his first art collection and the distilling of whiskey. Today, it is the development of Occidental Petroleum Corporation; the search for a cure for cancer through the Armand Hammer Center for Cancer Research at the Salk Institute in La Jolla, California; and the Julius and Armand Hammer Health Sciences Center at Columbia University, which is their alma mater. Not the least of his endeavors is the assembling of the present collection of works of art for the benefit of the public. The paintings will ultimately hang in the Los Angeles County Museum of Art, and the drawings are destined to hang in the National Gallery of Art.

He has also recently acquired a singular collection of works by Honoré Daumier and another of works by Daumier's contemporaries. The Daumier collection travels all over the world, as does the present one, to reach the greatest number of people. This too is destined to hang ultimately in the Los Angeles County Museum of Art, hopefully together with the paintings in the Frances and Armand Hammer wing.

Armand Hammer is not like other collectors. His delight is in the quest, not the possession. None of his great paintings or drawings hangs in his house. He is satisfied to live with a fine copy by Mrs. Hammer of the Modigliani portrait bought with his funds by the Los Angeles County Museum of Art, and with a few Impressionist paintings of lesser importance. Now in his eighties, he works as hard as anyone I have ever known. Much of his life is spent in his airplane flying from one place to another, tirelessly seeking to improve the earnings of Occidental Petroleum. He feels a deep sense of obligation to the shareholders, but he is also interested in making money himself. Why? For the sheer joy of giving it away. It may or may not be true that it is more blessed to give than to receive. But Armand Hammer would say it is certainly much more fun!

John Walker
Director Emeritus
National Gallery of Art, Washington, D.C.

Armand Hammer Collection Exhibitions

The Armand Hammer Collection has traveled to dozens of cities throughout the world since the collection was assembled in 1968. Listed below are the cities, institutions, and dates of the exhibitions in which the collection has been shown. In addition to these major installations, individual works are frequently lent to other exhibitions — or limited selections from the collection are shown as a unit — in the spirit of cultural exchange. Also, the collection is based in Los Angeles when it is not traveling and works from the collection are often hung with the permanent collection of the Los Angeles County Museum of Art.

The information provided in each entry of this catalogue includes provenance, exhibitions of the individual work before it entered the Armand Hammer Collection, exhibitions of the work outside the context of the whole collection, and an abbreviated listing of the Armand Hammer Collection exhibitions. Thus, the *Collections* heading indicates provenance, the *Exhibitions* heading indicates exhibitions of the work before and outside the context of the whole collection, and the *Armand Hammer Collection Exhibitions* heading indicates the major showings of the collection listed in full below.

New York, New York
 Hammer Galleries
 40th Anniversary Loan Exhibition, 1928-1968
 November 7-December 7, 1968

Memphis, Tennessee
 Brooks Memorial Art Gallery
 October 2-December 30, 1969

Washington, D.C.
 Smithsonian Institution
 The Armand Hammer Collection
 March 20-May 17, 1970

Kansas City, Missouri
 William Rockhill Nelson Gallery of Art
 June 30-August 2, 1970

New Orleans, Louisiana
 Isaac Delgado Museum of Art
 August 15-September 20, 1970

Columbus, Ohio
 Columbus Gallery of Fine Arts
 October 9-November 1, 1970

Little Rock, Arkansas
 Arkansas Art Center
 November 21, 1970-January 12, 1971

San Francisco, California
 California Palace of the Legion of Honor
 February 11-March 14, 1971

Oklahoma City, Oklahoma
 Oklahoma Art Center
 June 15-July 11, 1971

San Diego, California
 Fine Arts Gallery of San Diego
 July 30-September 5, 1971

Los Angeles, California
 Los Angeles County Museum of Art
 December 21, 1971-February 27, 1972

London, England
 Royal Academy of Arts
 June 24-July 24, 1972

Dublin, Ireland
 The National Gallery of Ireland
 August 9-October 1, 1972

Leningrad, U.S.S.R.
 The Hermitage Museum
 October 23-December 2, 1972

Moscow, U.S.S.R.
 The Pushkin Museum
 December 8, 1972-February 11, 1973

Kiev, U.S.S.R.
 State Museum of Fine Art of the
 Ukraine Soviet Socialist Republic
 March 6-March 31, 1973

Minsk, U.S.S.R.
 State Fine Art Museum
 April 27-May 26, 1973

Riga, U.S.S.R.
 State Museum of Foreign Fine Arts
 June 8-July 8, 1973

Odessa, U.S.S.R.
    Fine Arts Museum
    July 25-August 25, 1973

Los Angeles, California
    Los Angeles County Museum of Art
    June 22-December 9, 1974

Caracas, Venezuela
    Fine Arts Museum
    January 9-February 2, 1975

Lima, Peru
    Italian Art Museum
    February 15-March 9, 1975

Los Angeles, California
    Los Angeles County Museum of Art
    10th Anniversary Show
    April 9-June 29, 1975

Tokyo, Japan
    Ikebukuro-Seibu Museum
    September 20-November 3, 1975

Kyoto, Japan
    Municipal Museum of Art
    November 10-December 20, 1975

Fukuoka, Japan
    Fukuoka Prefectural Culture Center Museum
    January 4-February 1, 1976

Nagoya, Japan
    Aichi Prefectural Museum
    February 11-March 20, 1976

Nashville, Tennessee
    Tennessee Fine Arts Center at Cheekwood
    June 12-September 12, 1976

Mexico City, Mexico
    Palace of Fine Arts
    February 21-March 15, 1977

Paris, France
    Jacquemart-André Museum
    March 29-July 25, 1977

Paris, France
    Louvre Museum, Department of Drawings
    March 29-July 25, 1977

Malibu, California
    The J. Paul Getty Museum
    September 13-October 29, 1977

Atlanta, Georgia
    The High Museum of Art
    November 20, 1977-January 22, 1978

Denver, Colorado
    The Denver Art Museum
    February 18-April 9, 1978

Buffalo, New York
    Albright-Knox Art Gallery
    April 21-June 18, 1978

Edinburgh, Scotland
    The National Gallery of Scotland
    and the Royal Scottish Academy
    August 17-September 17, 1978

Oslo, Norway
    National Gallery of Norway
    December 8, 1978-January 28, 1979

Stockholm, Sweden
    Nationalmuseum
    February 20-April 22, 1979

Houston, Texas
    The Museum of Fine Arts
    October 26, 1979-January 20, 1980

Moultrie, Georgia
    The Moultrie-Colquitt County Library
    February 1-February 14, 1980

Los Angeles, California
    Los Angeles County Museum of Art
    April 24-August 31, 1980

Washington, D.C.
    The Corcoran Gallery of Art
    October 4-November 30, 1980

West Palm Beach, Florida
    The Norton Gallery of Art
    January 20-March 15, 1981

Cincinnati, Ohio
    Cincinnati Art Museum
    April 18-June 7, 1981

Paintings

Rembrandt van Rijn 1606-1669
b. Leiden, Holland   *d.* Amsterdam

1   *Juno,* ca. 1662-65
    Oil on canvas 127.0 x 122.87 cm.

Collections: Harmen Becker, Amsterdam, between 1665 and 1678; possibly Sir John Thomas Stanley, Palmerston House, Turnbridge, England, and his heirs, 1766-1850; Otto Friedrich Ludwig Wesendonck, Berlin, 1888-96, and his heirs, until 1925; Rheinische Provinzialverband and the City of Bonn, 1925-35 (sold Math. Lempertz, Cologne, Nov. 27, 1935); W. Poech and A. J. Schrender, Amsterdam, purchased at Cologne sale, 1935; D. Katz, Dieren, the Netherlands, 1935; C.J.K. van Aalst, K.B.E., Huis te Hoevelaken, the Netherlands, by 1939, and his heirs, until 1966; Hans M. Cramer, The Hague, 1966; Mr. and Mrs. J. William Middendorf II, 1966.

Exhibitions: Bonn, Provinzialmuseum, 1906-35, lent by the heirs of Mr. Otto Wesendonck until 1925; Amsterdam, Rijksmuseum, *Internal Art Trade Exhibition,* 1935; New York, Schaeffer Galleries, Inc., *Rembrandt,* Apr. 1-15, 1937 (no. 5), lent by D. Katz, repr. in cat.; New York World's Fair, *Masterpieces of European Paintings and Sculpture from 1300 to 1800,* May-Oct. 1939 (no. 312), lent by C.J.K. van Aalst, p. 52 in cat. by G. H. McCall and W. R. Valentiner; Detroit Institute of Arts, *Masterpieces of Art from Foreign Collections* (European paintings from the New York and San Francisco World's Fairs), Nov. 10-Dec. 10, 1939 (no. 40), lent by C.J.K. van Aalst, repr. in cat.; circulated in 1940-41 to Cleveland Museum of Art, Los Angeles County Museum of Art, Minneapolis Institute of Arts, Newark Museum, Springfield Museum, Springfield, Mass., and City Art Museum of St. Louis; Detroit Institute of Arts, *Masterpieces of Art from European and American Collections* (European paintings from the New York and San Francisco World's Fairs), Apr. 1-May 31, 1941 (no. 49), lent by C.J.K. van Aalst, repr. in cat. p. 18; Detroit Institute of Arts, 1941-47, lent by C.J.K. van Aalst; Los Angeles County Museum of Art, *Frans Hals-Rembrandt,* Nov. 18-Dec. 31, 1947 (no. 30), lent by Estate of C.J.K. van Aalst, pp. 74-75, plate XXX in cat. by W. R. Valentiner; Rotterdam, Museum Boymans van Beuningen, Mar.-May 1966, lent by Mr. and Mrs. J. William Middendorf II; New York, Metropolitan Museum of Art, 1966-1976, lent by Mr. and Mrs. J. William Middendorf II; New York, Wildenstein & Co., Inc., *Gods & Heroes, Baroque Images of Antiquity,* Oct. 30-Dec. 30, 1968 (no. 34), lent by Mr. and Mrs. J. William Middendorf II, color frontispiece in cat.; Kyoto, Municipal Museum, Jan. 3-Mar. 1, 1969, *The Age of Rembrandt, Dutch Paintings and Drawings of the 17th Century* (no. 52), lent by Mr. and Mrs. J. William Middendorf II; Cambridge, Mass., Fogg Art Museum, Harvard University, Oct. 6-Dec. 13, 1976; Los Angeles County Museum of Art, New Acquisitions Gallery, Dec. 19, 1976-Feb. 6, 1977.

Armand Hammer Collection Exhibitions: see pp. 17-18.
First exhibited Mexico City, 1977. Not exhibited Moultrie.

Literature: N. De Roever, "Rembrandt, Bijdrogen tot de Geschiedenis van zijn laatste levensjaren," *Oud Holland,* vol. 2 (1884) pp. 90-91; O. Wesendonck, *Katalog A. Gemälde Sammlung Wesendonck,* Berlin, 1888, pp. 77-78, no. 240; A. Bredius, *"Nievwe Rembrandtiana," Oud Holland,* vol. 17 (1899), p. 4; C. Hofstede de Groot, *Die Urkunden über Rembrandt (1575-1721),* The Hague, 1906, pp. 337-38, no. 278, pp. 340-41, no. 280, pp. 341-42, no. 281; W. Cohen, "Die Sammlung Wesendonck," *Zeitschrift für Bildende Kunst,* n.s., vol. 21 (1909), pp. 57 ff.; A. Bredius, "Rembrandtiana II: De Nalatenschap van Harmen Becker," *Oud Holland,* vol. 28 (1910), pp. 195 ff.; W. Cohen, *Katalog der Gemäldegalerie vorwiegend Sammlung Wesendonck,* Provinzialmuseum, Bonn, 1914, p. 156 (2nd ed., 1927, p. 154), no. 230; C. Hofstede de Groot, *A Catalogue Raisonné of the Works of the Most Eminent Dutch Painters of the Seventeenth Century,* London, 1916, vol. 6, p. 138, no. 207a; *Westdeutscher Museumbesitz, Sammlung Wesendonck von Bissing,* sale catalogue, Math. Lempertz, Cologne, 1935, p. 26, no. 87, repr.; A. Bredius, "Ein wiedergefundener Rembrandt," *Pantheon,* vol. 18 (1936), p. 277, repr.; A. Bredius, *The Paintings of Rembrandt,* 2nd ed., London, 1937, p. 27, no. 639, repr.; A. Heppner, "Ein Rembrandt Entedeckung," *Die Weltkunst,* vol. 8, nos. 31-32 (Aug. 9, 1936), p. 1, repr.; G. Isarlo, "La Juno de Rembrandt est retrouvée," *Beaux-arts,* Oct. 9, 1936, p. 2, repr.; J.L.A.A.M. dan Ryckevorsel, "De Teruggevonden Schilderij van Rembrandt: De Juno," *Oud Holland,* vol. 53 (1936), pp. 270-74, plate 1; H. G. Fell, "The 'Juno' of Rembrandt," *Connoisseur,* vol. 99 (Jan.-June 1937), p. 3, repr. in color frontispiece and on cover (includes letters by A. Bredius and W. R. Valentiner); "Rembrandt's 'Juno,' " *The Art Designer,* vol. 11, no. 13 (Apr. 1, 1937), p. 12, repr.; A. M. Frankfurter, "An Important View of Rembrandt," *The Art News,* vol. 35, no. 27 (Apr. 3, 1937), pp. 9, 24-25, repr. p. 8; J. Held, "Two Rembrandts," *Parnassus,* vol. 9, no. 4 (Apr. 1937), pp. 36-38, repr.; M. Weinberger, " 'New' Rembrandts," *Magazine of Art,* vol. 30 (1937), pp. 312-14, repr. p. 299; John Rewald, "A l'étranger un Rembrandt vendu par un musée allemand," *Amour de l'art,* vol. 19, no. 9 (Nov. 1938), p. 361, repr.; W. R. Valentiner and A. M. Frankfurter, *Masterpieces of Art, Exhibition at the New York World's Fair 1939 — Guide and Picture Book,* New York, 1939, repr. p. 96; E. Kieser, "Uber Rembrandts Verhältnis zur Antike," *Zeitschrift für Kunstgeschichte,* vol. 10 (1941-42), p. 141; Jakob Rosenberg, *Rembrandt,* Cambridge, Mass., 1948, vol. 1, p. 248 (concordance); G. Knuttel, *Rembrandt, De meester en zijn werk,* Amsterdam, 1956, pp. 210, 278; "Rembrandt's 'Lost' Juno to be Auctioned at Christie's," *Arts,* vol. 34, no. 5 (Feb. 1960), p. 9; N. MacLaren, *The Dutch School,* catalogue, National Gallery, London, 1960, p. 313; *Highly Important Netherlandish Paintings from the Collection Formed by the Late Dr. C.J.K van Aalst,* sale catalogue (painting not sold), Christie, Manson, & Woods, London, Apr. 1, 1960, pp. 26-27, no. 38, plate 18 and color frontispiece; *Catalogue No. XII 1965-66,* G. Cramer Galerie, The Hague, 1965, p. 7, repr.; G.C.V., "Rembrandt 'Juno' in den Haag," *Die Weltkunst,* vol. 35, no. 21 (Nov. 15, 1965), pp. 109-192; Kurt Bauch, *Rembrandt Gemälde,* Berlin, 1966, pp. XV, 15, no. 285, repr.; "Rembrandt's 'Juno' für das Metropolitan Museum," *Die Weltkunst,* vol. 36, no. 7 (Apr. 1, 1966), p. 291, repr.; Ann Livermore, "Rembrandt and Jansen: A New Interpretation," *Apollo,* vol. 85 (Jan.-June 1967), p. 245, note 4; Horst Gerson,

Rembrandt's Paintings, Amsterdam and New York, 1968, pp. 132-33, 430-31, repr. in color; S. Nodelman, "After the High Roman Fashion," *Art News,* vol. 67, no. 7 (Nov. 1968), pp. 34 ff., repr.; J. T. Butler, "The American Way with Art," *Connoisseur,* vol. 169 (Nov. 1968), p. 200, repr.; M. S. Young, "Letter from U.S.A.," *Apollo,* vol. 87 (July-Dec. 1968), p. 390; J. J. Jacobs, "New York Gallery Notes," *Art in America,* vol. 56, no. 6 (Nov.-Dec. 1968), p. 109, repr. in color; *The Age of Rembrandt, Dutch Paintings and Drawings of the 17th Century,* catalogue, National Museum of Western Art, Tokyo, and Municipal Museum, Kyoto, 1968-69, no. 52, repr.; Horst Gerson (ed.), *Rembrandt, The Complete Edition of the Paintings of Rembrandt by A. Bredius,* London, 1969, p. 617, no. 639, repr. p. 396; J. Held, *Rembrandt's Aristotle and Other Rembrandt Studies,* Princeton, N. J., 1969, chap. 3, pp. 85-103, repr.; B. Haak, *Rembrandt, His Life, His Work, His Time,* New York, 1969, p. 318, repr. in color p. 318, plate 539; Egbert Haverkamp-Begemann, "The Present State of Rembrandt Studies," *Art Bulletin,* vol. 53 (1971), p. 95.

In Rembrandt's *Juno,* the queen of the gods confronts us squarely, a robust young woman of ample proportions, opulently dressed, with a golden crown on her head and a golden scepter in her hand. Most of the artist's contemporaries would have readily recognized that the peacock at her side is her traditional attribute. The ancient gods were still very much alive in the minds of seventeenth century Dutchmen. They were introduced to them at an early age — Rembrandt began his study of classical culture when he was a boy of seven — and the numerous references to the gods in the literature of the period show that familiarity with them was taken for granted.

Dutchmen of Rembrandt's epoch knew that the ancients gave Juno many roles. She was venerated as a goddess of the state, a deity of the moon, the goddess of marriage, and the protectress of women — particularly of those in childbirth. They also knew that Boccaccio and later writers and artists popularized her as the goddess of wealth.

Which role did Rembrandt assign to his *Juno,* and for whom did he paint it? Everything that is known about the painting's history and style, as well as what has been learned about it through technical analysis in the laboratory, supports the conclusion that Rembrandt painted Juno as the goddess of wealth for Harmen Becker, a rich Amsterdam merchant, moneylender, and collector.

Contemporary documents tell us that about 1662-63 Becker made two loans to Rembrandt. The artist gave Becker nine of his paintings and two volumes of his prints and drawings as collateral. In 1664 one of Rembrandt's close friends went to Becker on his behalf to repay the principal and interest on the two loans. Becker refused to accept payment. A notarized statement declares that at the time of his refusal Becker said, "Let Rembrandt first finish the *Juno.*" In the following year, the litigation between Rembrandt and Becker was amicably resolved; thus, by 1665 Rembrandt had finished the painting to Becker's satisfaction.

Rembrandt van Rijn
Juno, detail

The style of the *Juno* strengthens the evidence that it was this picture that was the nub of the controversy between Becker and Rembrandt. The pronounced frontality of the goddess, the even light that plays over her broadly displayed figure, the spontaneous and flexible brushwork combined with subtle glazing, and the powerful coloristic harmonies are compatible with a date of about 1662-65 for the imposing painting.

X-ray radiography has recently revealed some new evidence that may cast light on Becker's displeasure at the delayed delivery of the *Juno*. The artist made a major alteration in the painting. He originally painted Juno's right arm in a position almost symmetrical to her left, with both of her hands resting on a ledge or a table. Then he had a second thought. He raised her right arm to the present position and gave the goddess her scepter. Possibly Rembrandt began to make this change and then stopped working on the picture; we know that he never won a reputation for finishing his commissions rapidly. Perhaps Becker was irritated by the delay the change caused and so declared, "Let Rembrandt first finish the *Juno*."

Alternatively, Becker may have insisted that passages of economic brushwork and impasto touches needed a higher degree of finish. If this was the issue, Rembrandt must have finally convinced his patron of the validity of his axiom that, "A painting is finished when the artist has completed his intention." The summary brushwork and fluctuating impasto passages remain, heightening the pictorial effect.

In any event, Becker received and kept the painting. It is listed in the inventory made of his effects after his death in 1678. His inventory also lists a second, unattributed, life-size painting of *Juno*, an indication that the rich merchant had a special interest in the goddess of wealth. We also know that Becker had a passion for Rembrandt's work. In addition to the *Juno*, his inventory lists fourteen other paintings by the master.

Nothing is known of the whereabouts of the *Juno* from 1678 until the eighteenth to mid-nineteenth century, although there is reason to believe that it was in an English private collection. By 1888 it was in the possession of the Berlin merchant Otto Wesendonck. The work's subsequent history is worth telling.

After Wesendonck's death, his heirs put the *Juno* on loan at the Bonn Provinzialmuseum. When it was catalogued there in 1914, it was listed not as an original Rembrandt but erroneously demoted to the status of a work by one of the artist's anonymous imitators. The provincial Council of the Rhineland and the City of Bonn acquired the painting in 1925. Not long after the Nazis came to power in 1933, the Bonn museum officials were ordered to concentrate on Rhenish art and sell their holdings unrelated to their new mandate. In compliance with this order, the painting was auctioned at Cologne in 1935 as a work in the "style of Rembrandt," and it fetched 900 marks at the sale. Soon afterward, experts recognized the *Juno*, not only as an indisputable original but as one of the finest and best-documented late works by Holland's greatest artist.

S.S.

Rembrandt van Rijn 1606-1669

2   *Portrait of a Man Holding a Black Hat,* ca. 1637
    Oil on panel 81.7 x 71.0 cm.
    Signed, lower right: *Rembrandt*

Collections: In 1836 John Smith catalogued a portrait included in the Proley sale of 1787, which
C. Hofstede de Groot, concluded was identical with his painting *(A Catalogue Raisonné of the Works of
the Most Eminent Dutch Painters of the Seventeenth Century).* Hofstede de Groot noted that the Proley
sale took place in Paris, but efforts to trace a catalogue of the sale have been unsuccessful; Prince
Nicolas Gagarin, Moscow, by 1906; sold by Prince Gagarin through Prince Pierre Troubteskoy to Alfred
W. Erickson, New York, 1925; Mr. and Mrs. J. William Middendorf II, 1961-79.

Exhibitions: Detroit Institute of Arts, *Paintings by Rembrandt,* May 2-31, 1930 (no. 28), lent by
A. W. Erickson, repr. in cat. as *Prince Frederick Henry, Governor of the Netherlands,* dated 1637;
New York, Metropolitan Museum of Art, 1961-79, lent by Mr. and Mrs. J. William Middendorf II, as
Prince Frederick of Orange, dated 1637; Washington, D.C., National Gallery of Art, 1979, lent by
the Armand Hammer Foundation.

Armand Hammer Collection Exhibitions: see pp. 17-18.
First exhibited Houston, 1979-80. Not exhibited Moultrie.

Literature: Possibly identical with no. 263, *A Gentleman, Seen in Three-quarter View, Habited in the
Ancient Dutch Costume, and Holding His Hat in His Hand,* in John Smith, *Catalogue Raisonné of the
Works of the Most Eminent Dutch, Flemish and French Painters,* London, 1836, vol. 7, p. 99, panel,
72.5 x 65.0 cm., collection of Proley, 1787; Wilhelm Bode and C. Hofstede de Groot, *The Complete Work
of Rembrandt,* Paris, 1906, vol. 8, p. 102, no. 570, repr., as *A Young Man in Profile Holding His Hat in
Both Hands,* dated 1637; Wilhelm R. Valentiner, *Rembrandt, des Meisters Gemälde* (Klassiker der Kunst),
3rd ed., Stuttgart and Berlin, 1909, repr. p. 217, as *Portrait of a Young Man,* dated 1637 and described by
Valentiner, p. 536, as perhaps a portrait of Prince Frederick Henry, stadtholder of the Netherlands;
C. Hofstede de Groot, *A Catalogue Raisonné of the Works of the Most Eminent Dutch Painters of the
Seventeenth Century,* London, 1916, vol. 6, p. 353, no. 751, as *A Young Man Holding a High Broad
Rimmed Hat with Both Hands,* dated 1637; Wilhelm R. Valentiner, *Rembrandt Paintings in America,*
New York, 1931, no. 62, as *Prince Frederick Henry, Governor of the Netherlands,* dated 1637; Jakob
Rosenberg, *Rembrandt,* Cambridge, Mass., 1948, vol. 1, p. 248 (concordance); A. Staring, "Vraagstukken
der Oranje-Iconographie III. Conterfeite Rembrandt Frederik Hendrik en Amalia?" *Oud Holland,* vol. 68
(1953), p. 14, not described as a portrait of Frederick Henry; *Old Master Paintings Collected by the Late
Mr. and Mrs. Alfred W. Erickson,* sale catalogue, New York, Nov. 15, 1961, listed as *Prince Frederick
Henry of Orange, Governor of the Netherlands,* and described as dated, almost illegibly, 1637; Jakob
Rosenberg, *Rembrandt: Life and Work,* London, 1964, p. 371 (concordance); Kurt Bauch, *Rembrandt
Gemälde,* Berlin, 1966, no. 379, repr., as *Prince Frederick Henry of Orange-Nassau, Stadtholder of the
Netherlands (?),* dated 1637, and described by Bauch, p. 20, no. 379, as *Portrait of a Distinguished Man,*
noting the unlikelihood that the work is a portrait of Frederick Henry.

Since this portrait was catalogued in 1906, every published reference to it has stated that it was signed and dated 1637. When it was sold in 1961, a qualification regarding its inscription was introduced; the author of the sale catalogue scrupulously noted that the date had become almost illegible. Today the date has completely disappeared; but to judge from the painting's style, there is little reason to doubt the date recorded by earlier specialists. This "swagger" portrait is characteristic of the fashionable ones Rembrandt painted during the mid-1630s, when his reputation as a painter of likenesses was at its zenith.

Not long after the painting became generally known, it was tentatively identified as a portrait of Frederick Henry, Prince of Orange-Nassau. Soon afterward this suggestion was accepted by some people without reservation. It is not hard to understand why — the reported discovery of a portrait by Holland's greatest artist of a leading hero of his country was a boost to national pride.

As every Dutch schoolchild knows, Frederick Henry was a son of William the Silent, the principal leader of the Dutch struggle for independence from Spain. In 1625 Frederick Henry succeeded his older brother, Maurice, as hereditary stadtholder of the United Provinces of the Netherlands and commander-in-chief of its armies. The prince's military victories and political skills helped end the bitter eighty-year war between Spain and the Netherlands. He died in 1647, a year before the Treaty of Münster finally established peace between the two nations and accorded the new Dutch Republic *de jure* recognition among the family of nations.

Knowledge that Rembrandt enjoyed the prince's patronage helped lend credibility to the identification of the subject of this portrait as Frederick Henry. As early as 1632, only a year after the artist had made his debut as a professional portraitist, he painted a likeness of Frederick Henry's consort, Amalia van Solms. A few years later, the prince acquired Rembrandt's *Raising of the Cross* and *Descent from the Cross,* and by 1636 had commissioned Rembrandt to paint three additional scenes from the Passion: an *Entombment,* a *Resurrection,* and an *Ascension of Christ.* The prince not only continued to collect Rembrandt's pictures but was willing to pay top prices for them. In 1646 he instructed his treasurer to send the artist the very substantial sum of 2,400 guilders for two of his paintings, an *Adoration of the Shepherds* and a *Circumcision of Christ.*

In view of the prince's record as a loyal patron of the artist, it would almost seem unnatural if he had not commissioned Rembrandt to paint his own portrait. He seems in fact to have ordered one — if we can trust the attribution made by the author of an inventory compiled in 1667 of a collection in a palace that belonged to the House of Orange at The Hague. The inventory lists a profile portrait of His Highness Prince Frederick Henry by Rembrandt. There is, however, good reason to believe that the compiler of the 1667 inventory muddled matters by wrongly ascribing to Rembrandt a profile portrait of the prince by Gerrit van Honthorst, a portrait still in the royal collection at The Hague. In any event, this portrait cannot be identical with the Armand Hammer painting; it is specifically described as a portrait done in profile. The man in the Hammer painting is seen almost full face.

Frederick Henry enhanced cultural life at his court in The Hague, but in the prince's time his fame was not founded upon his promotion of the arts. It rested on his brilliance as a military strategist, his gifts as a statesman, and his reputation as a ladies' man. Before his marriage at the age of forty to Amalia van Solms, he was reputed to have been too fond of women to tie himself permanently to one. Nothing about Rembrandt's portrayal appears to contradict this characterization of the prince, but of course it is impossible to determine the degree of a man's fondness for the company of women from an artist's portrayal of him!

Identification of the painting as a portrait of Frederick Henry can rest neither upon the prince's proven patronage of Rembrandt nor on unprovable interpretations of the attitude of the artist's client toward women. Identification can be tested, however, by checking the resemblance of the man in this painting to the documented portraits of the prince by Anthony van Dyck and by Gerrit van Honthorst. A comparison of these pictures (which predictably shows the prince in armor accompanied by symbols of authority) with the Hammer portrait shatters the appealing idea that Rembrandt's painting is a likeness of the prince. Compared to the person painted by these other artists, Rembrandt's sitter resembles Frederick Henry as much as George Washington resembles Paul Revere.

Although the man who commissioned Rembrandt to paint his portrait must join the large ranks of the artist's anonymous patrons, it is possible to deduce a few things about him. Apart from the good taste and judgment he showed when he selected Rembrandt as his portraitist in the 1630s, it is evident that he did not share his contemporaries' taste for somber black clothing. He chose to be painted in a gray moiré jacket. He must have been delighted with Rembrandt's nearly miraculous shifts in color and tone that allowed the artist to suggest the way light is variously reflected from the heavily and irregularly ribbed threads of his taffeta jacket, producing watered and rippled effects. The intense realism that characterizes Rembrandt's paintings of this period and the high standard of pictorial richness and execution he maintained are evident in other key passages of this fine portrait, most notably in the artist's characterization of his handsome patron's face. Rembrandt's genius enabled him to accentuate his deep human interest while giving an unrivaled virtuoso display of his ability to render the color, texture, and weight of materials.

S.S.

Rembrandt van Rijn 1606-1669

3 *Portrait of a Man of the Raman Family,* 1634
Oil on oval panel 64.8 x 50.5 cm. enlarged to a rectangle 68.8 x 53.2 cm.
Signed and dated, lower right: *Rembrandt fe 1634*
Inscribed, lower left: *Ae. 47*

Collections: Raman Family, Amsterdam; August de Ridder, Schönberg near Cronberg, before 1909 (sold Galerie Georges Petit, Paris, June 2, 1924 (no. 55)); Ehrich Galleries, New York, 1930-36; N. Katz, Basel, by 1948 (sold Paris, Apr. 25, 1951); Julius Weitzner Galleries, New York, by 1956; P. de Boer, Amsterdam, before 1966; H. Kohn, Wassenaar, the Netherlands, by 1968; H. Shickman Gallery, New York, 1969; Dr. and Mrs. Armand Hammer; Los Angeles County Museum of Art (Frances and Armand Hammer Purchase Fund, 1969).

Exhibitions: Frankfurt-am-Main, Städelsches Kunstinstitut, 1911-13 (following the death of De Ridder, May 13, 1911); New York, F. Kleinberger Galleries, *The Collection of Pictures of the Late Herr A. de Ridder,* exhibition and private sale, Nov. 24-Dec. 15, 1913 (no. 1); Detroit Institute of Arts, *Paintings by Rembrandt,* May 2-31, 1930 (no. 22), lent by Ehrich Galleries, New York, repr. in cat.; The Hague, Mauritshuis, *Herwonnen Kunstbezit: Tentoonstelling van uit Duitschland Teruggekeerde Nederlandsche Kunstschatten,* Mar.-May 1946 (no. 49); Basel, Katz Galerie, *Rembrandt Ausstellung,* July 24-Sept. 30, 1948 (no. 13), lent by Swiss private collector, repr. in cat.; Raleigh, North Carolina Museum of Art, Nov. 16-Dec. 30, 1956 (no. 9), lent by Julius Weitzner, repr. in cat.

Armand Hammer Collection Exhibitions: see pp. 17-18.
First exhibited Memphis, 1969. Not exhibited Kansas City; New Orleans; Columbus; Little Rock; San Francisco; Oklahoma City; San Diego; Los Angeles, 1974; Los Angeles, 1975; Moultrie.

Literature: W. R. Valentiner, *Rembrandt, des Meisters Gemälde* (Klassiker der Kunst), 3rd ed., Stuttgart and Berlin, 1909, repr. p. 193, as *Portrait of a Man*; Wilhelm Bode, *Die Gemäldegalerie des Herrn A. de Ridder,* Berlin, 1910, pp. 4, 35, plate 1, as *Portrait of a Man of the Raman Family*; Wilhelm Bode, *The Collection of Pictures of the Late Herr A. de Ridder* (trans. Harry Virgin), Berlin, 1913, no. 1, plate 1; C. Hofstede de Groot, *A Catalogue Raisonné of the Works of the Most Eminent Dutch Painters of the Seventeenth Century,* London, 1916, vol. 6, p. 347, no. 739, as *A Man in a Large Slouch Hat, said to be a member of the Raman family; Catalogue des tableaux anciens . . . composant la galerie de feu M. A. de Ridder,* sale catalogue, Galerie Georges Petit, Paris, 1924, no. 55, repr.; A. Bredius, *Rembrandt Gemälde,* Vienna, 1935, p. 9, no. 194, repr.; A. Bredius, *The Paintings of Rembrandt,* 2nd ed., London, 1937, p. 8, no. 194, repr.; Jakob Rosenberg, *Rembrandt,* Cambridge, Mass., 1948, vol. 1, p. 243 (concordance); Kurt Bauch, *Rembrandt Gemälde,* Berlin, 1966, p. 19 (notes), no. 374, repr.; Horst Gerson, *Rembrandt Paintings,* Amsterdam and New York, 1968, p. 495, no. 168, repr. p. 289; Horst Gerson (ed.), *Rembrandt, The Complete Edition of the Paintings of Rembrandt by A. Bredius,* London, 1969, p. 564, no. 194, repr. p. 158; Mahonri Sharp Young, "The Hammer Collection: Paintings," *Apollo,* vol. 95 (June 1972), pp. 444, 446.

Rembrandt van Rijn
Portrait of a Man of the Raman Family, detail

When Rembrandt was seven years old, his father enrolled him in the Latin School at Leiden. His father, a miller, evidently was ambitious for him, since in his time only boys who were expected to study at a university and then go on to the ministry, law, medicine, or another profession were sent to learn Latin and read the classical authors. After spending seven years at the school, Rembrandt matriculated at Leiden University, but he soon dropped out. A contemporary tells us that the fourteen-year-old youth had no appetite for academic studies; his only interest was in painting and drawing.

Rembrandt appeared on the scene as an independent artist four or five years later. It was evident from the very beginning that he had high ambitions for himself. Most Dutch artists specialized in portraiture or realistic scenes. Rembrandt was made of different stuff; he was determined to make his mark as a painter of biblical, historical, and mythological subjects. He accepted the idea implicitly or explicitly endorsed by artists and theorists since the early Renaissance that such works were more significant than portraits, genre scenes, landscapes, and still lifes.

From about 1625 to 1630, Rembrandt mainly dedicated his art and volcanic energy to religious and classical subjects. His first commissioned portraits were done in 1631; and from that time until his last years, portraiture became his stock-in-trade. Nonetheless, he did not neglect the themes he considered more consequential. On the contrary, they continued to preoccupy him throughout his entire career and became his principal concern during his last phase. His *Juno* is an outstanding late example of this category of his work.

The vast number of commissioned portraits Rembrandt painted during the 1630s indicates that he quickly became the most sought-after painter of likenesses in Holland. His brilliant *Portrait of a Man of the Raman Family* shows the qualities that made his early reputation: a strong illusionism combined with pictorial effects that no other Dutch artists could match. We sense that Rembrandt provided a speaking likeness of his sitter as well as an accurate description of his clothing, two demands most people continue to make of portraitists. Any suggestion of hardness or overmeticulousness was avoided. Variety of touch and fluid brushwork subtly animate the features of his serious forty-seven-year-old patron, while the strong accent of light on the huge white ruff dissolves the forms of its complicated folds. In the handling of the light and shadow, there is no dramatic spotlight effect. The illuminated areas on the face are soft, the shadows transparent. The convincing roundness of forms is achieved by delicately graded half-tones, and variations in the values of the neutral background provide spaciousness and an atmosphere that envelops the figure.

The portrait belonged to the Raman family of Amsterdam until it was acquired by August de Ridder, before 1909. According to tradition, it has been in the possession of the Raman family since the seventeenth century; hence its title. When it was painted, oval formats for portraits were enjoying a vogue in Holland; at a later date, it was enlarged into a rectangle (the frame now hides the additions). The assumption that the *Portrait of a Woman in a Broad Ruff* of 1636, now in the collection of Lord Kinnaird, Rossie Priory, Perthshire, is a companion piece is supported by technical examinations that revealed the additions made to alter its shape from oval to rectangular as identical to the enlargements of the Hammer picture.

S.S.

Peter Paul Rubens 1577-1640
b. Siegen, Westphalia   *d.* Antwerp, Flanders

4   *Adoration of the Shepherds,* early 17th c.
Oil on canvas, formerly on panel 81.0 x 62.0 cm.

Collection: Erik W. Bergmann, Monroe, Mich.

Exhibitions: Los Angeles County Museum of Art, *Rubens and Van Dyck,* 1946 (no. 3), repr. in cat.;
Hollins, Va., Hollins College, 1954-55; Lynchburg, Va., Art Center, 1955; Charlottesville, Va., University
of Virginia, 1956; Cologne, Wallraf-Richartz Museum, *Rubens in Italien,* Oct. 15-Dec. 15, 1977 (no. 12);
San José, Costa Rica, Museo de Jade, *Five Centuries of Masterpieces from American Collections Loaned
to Costa Rica,* Apr. 12-July 20, 1978.

Armand Hammer Collection Exhibitions: see pp. 17-18.
First exhibited Oslo, 1979. Not exhibited Moultrie; West Palm Beach.

Literature: W. R. Valentiner, *Art Quarterly,* vol. 9 (1946), p. 155, no. 7, fig. 1, as Rubens between 1607
and 1608; Leo van Puyvelde, *Rubens,* Paris, 1952, p. 201, note 33; Erick Larsen, *P. P. Rubens,* Antwerp,
1952, p. 215, note 12, as related to the Fermo altarpiece but an independent composition by Rubens of
about 1608; W. R. Valentiner and P. Wescher, *The Hammer Collection,* Greenville, S.C., 1957, p. 43;
Michael Jaffé, *Proporzioni,* vol. 4 (1963), p. 233, notes 101 and 105, figs. 34 and 35, as Rubens between
1606 and 1607; *The Armand Hammer Collection,* University of Southern California, Los Angeles, 1965,
p. 49 (repr. in color on cover); Michael Jaffé, *Rubens and Italy,* Oxford, 1977, p. 98R, plate 337, as
Rubens independent of the Fermo altarpiece and about 1607; J. Müller Hofstede, *Rubens in Italien,*
catalogue, Wallraf-Richartz Museum, Cologne, 1977, no. 12, plate K-12, as Rubens after the Fermo
altarpiece, probably between June 7 and Oct. 28, 1608.

A Nativity at San Filippo in Fermo resembles
this *Adoration of the Shepherds* — also known as
The Nativity — but the theory that the Hammer
painting is a *modello* for the Fermo altarpiece is
now discounted by most scholars. Besides being
the reverse of the Fermo in composition, the
Hammer painting differs in the disposition of
the figures. It appears to be an independent
treatment of the subject and, according to
Michael Jaffé, may anticipate the Fermo
altarpiece by some months. Jaffé tentatively
suggests the name of Father Flamminio Ricci as
the original recipient of this small panel. Ricci
was Rubens' patron among the Oratorian
Fathers and was responsible for the Fermo
commission. J. Müller Hofstede thinks the
Hammer painting could have been painted after
the Fermo altarpiece, between June 7 and
October 28, 1608 (the date of Rubens' return to
Flanders). He notes that it was not painted on
coarse canvas, as was usual in Italy, but on fine
canvas. Therefore, the possibility cannot be
excluded that Rubens painted this version in
Antwerp after his return to Flanders in 1609.
Both Jaffé and Müller Hofstede refute the

statement by W. R. Valentiner and P. Wescher
that this *Adoration* once belonged to Duke Carlos
II of Mantua. Müller Hofstede notes that the
Nativity at Mantua was listed as being
"un braccio e mezzo" (approximately 100.0 cm.),
a figure that rules out the possibility that this
is the picture in the Hammer Collection.

According to Leo van Puyvelde, the present
Adoration could be the little *Nativity* referred to
in the inventory of Rubens' studio made at the
time of his death. There are at least two
drawings related to figures in the Hammer
picture, both in reverse: one corresponds to the
head of Joseph (Frits Lugt Coll.; first published
by Julius S. Held (*Rubens, Selected Drawings,*
1959, repr. vol. 2, plate 154)) and the other to the
head of the young peasant woman with a basket
who kneels in the center of the Hammer canvas
(*Study of a Youth,* Mr. and Mrs. Robert L.
Manning Coll., Forest Hills, N.Y.; first published
by Jaffé (*Rubens and Italy,* plate 180)). While
Rubens was in Italy from 1600 to 1608, he often
chose his traveling companion and pupil,
Deodato van der Mont, as a model. It may be his
face that was used for the adoring shepherdess.

M.E.

Peter Paul Rubens 1577-1640

5   *Young Woman with Curly Hair,* ca. 1618-20
     Oil on panel 43.3 x 33.5 cm. enlarged to 67.0 x 52.4 cm.

Collections: M. Schamp d'Aveschoot, Ghent, recorded 1830 (sold Ghent, Sept. 14, 1840); Duc d'Arenberg and descendants, Brussels and later south of France, purchased 1840 at Schamp sale; Edward Speelman, London, purchased 1959 from present duke; Jean Davray, Paris; M. Knoedler & Co., New York, in 1967.

Armand Hammer Collection Exhibitions: see pp. 17-18.
First exhibited Memphis, 1969. Not exhibited Los Angeles, 1974; Los Angeles, 1975; Moultrie.

Literature: John Smith, *Catalogue Raisonné of the Works of the . . . Dutch, Flemish and French Painters,* vol. 2, London, 1830, pp. 260-61, no. 881, and vol. 9 (supplement), 1842, p. 330, no. 317; *Catalogue des tableaux . . . composant la galerie de M. Schamp d'Aveschoot, de Gand,* sale catalogue, Sept. 14, 1840, p. 2; Max Rooses, *L'Oeuvre de Pierre-Paul Rubens,* Antwerp, 1886-92, vol. 4, pp. 138, 290, no. 1088, as a repetition by Rubens of the Dresden picture, both of ca. 1635; J. Nève, "Quelques portraits de la galerie d'Arenberg," *Annales de l'Académie Royale d'Archéologie de Belgique,* Antwerp, vol. 5, ser. 4, tome 10 (1897), pp. 175-76; Max Rooses, "Oeuvres de Rubens — addenda," *Bulletin Rubens* (Antwerp), vol. 5 (1909), pp. 83-84; Rudolf Oldenbourg, *P. P. Rubens,* Munich and Berlin, 1922, p. 142; Ludwig Burchard, "Portrait of a Young Woman with Curly Hair by Peter Paul Rubens," ms. report on the Arenberg-Hammer painting, ca. 1960; Douglas Cooper (ed.), *Great Private Collections,* London, 1963, repr. p. 254, as ca. 1635; Michael Jaffé, Cambridge University, to Roland Balay, M. Knoedler & Co., New York, Feb. 3, 1967; Michael Harvard, "Portrait of a Girl with Curly Hair by Rubens," ms. report on the Arenberg-Hammer and Morris paintings, London, Mar. 1969; Michael Jaffé, "The Girl with the Golden Hair," *Apollo,* vol. 90 (Oct. 1969), pp. 310-13, repr. in color p. 311, plate IX; Mahonri Sharp Young, "The Hammer Collection: Paintings," *Apollo,* vol. 95 (June 1972), pp. 446, 451, repr. plate II in color, p. 441.

Peter Paul Rubens
Young Woman with Curly Hair, detail

The portrait as Rubens painted it was only the head and shoulders of the young woman. A seventeenth century copy in the Staatliche Gemäldegalerie in Kassel shows the portrait in its original rectangular shape and size before any of the enlargements. Sometime before the middle of the eighteenth century, the beveled edge (about 2.5 cm. all around) was trimmed off and the painting was set into a larger oval panel. Later, this oval was pieced out at the corners to make the present rectangle.

The subject of the Hammer picture must have been extraordinarily popular in the seventeenth and eighteenth centuries, for at least six early repetitions of it are known: the copy in the Staatliche Gemäldegalerie in Kassel of the original before enlargement (canvas, 43.8 x 34.9 cm., no. 89 in cat. of 1888); four repetitions of the present enlarged image; the oldest version in the Staatliche Kunstsammulungen, Dresden (panel, 64.1 x 49.5 cm., p. 93 in cat. of 1966, repr. in Adolf Rosenberg, *P. P. Rubens, des Meisters Gemälde* (Klassiker de Kunst), 2nd ed., Stuttgart and Leipzig, 1906, p. 373); Leningrad, Hermitage Museum (canvas, said to have been transferred from panel, 66.0 x 53.9 cm., no. 1692 in cat. of 1958, with additional drapery across the chest and near the shoulder); Althrop, The Earl Spencer Collection (untraceable, but known to Dr. Ludwig Burchard in 1947 and 1960 from a Hanfstaengl photograph, no. 113, showing two jeweled clasps holding the bodice); Kiel, Professor Gotz Maritus in 1935 (panel 58.1 x 42.8 cm.), similar to the Spencer portrait; and a sixth painting, still further enlarged, in the collection of John C. Morris, Richmond, Surrey. The Morris painting (panel 71.1 x 59.0 cm., repr. in Rudolf Oldenbourg, *P. P. Rubens, des Meisters Gemälde* (Klassiker der Kunst), 4th ed., Berlin and Leipzig, 1921 (p. 201)) has a slightly lower neckline and extends the torso almost to the hips. Michael Jaffé believes that all these repetitions of the enlarged picture were made after Rubens' death and that only the Hammer picture is an original by Rubens.

The identity of the sitter is not known. Jaffé believes that the painting is a study rather than a formal portrait. According to Burchard, Rubens made a second study of the same girl but in a more frontal pose (Munich, Alte Pinakothek, no. 793 in cat.; exhibited in Bamberg Museum in 1934). The Munich painting measures 47.9 x 36.8 cm., approximately the same as the Hammer painting originally and, in Burchard's opinion, was probably painted at the same sitting.

K.D.

Peter Paul Rubens 1577-1640

6   *The Israelites Gathering Manna in the Desert,* 1625-28
    Oil on panel 64.8 x 52.7 cm.

Collections: Isabella Clara Eugenia, Archduchess of the Spanish Netherlands, Brussels; Philip IV and Charles II of Spain(?); Dukes of Infantado to the 13th duke (d. 1841) listed in inventory of ca. 1800; Duke of Pastrana, Madrid (d. 1888), by inheritance from Duke of Infantado, natural father; Emile Pacully, Paris, from Duke of Pastrana or estate, private sale; Guy Stein, Paris, acquired at sale *Tableau...dépendant de la succession de M. E. Pacully,* Paris, Hôtel Drouot, July 5, 1938, (no. 28), repr. with added garland. (This and several other pictures from sale *Collection Emile Pacully, tableaux anciens et modernes,* Paris, Galerie Georges Petit, May 4, 1903, pp. 62-63, had apparently been bought back by owner and kept through his lifetime); Baron Robert Gendebien, Brussels, from G. Stein, dealer, 1938; Rosenberg & Stiebel, New York; Dr. and Mrs. Armand Hammer; Los Angeles County Museum of Art (Frances and Armand Hammer Purchase Fund, 1969).

Exhibitions: *Exhibition of a Collection of Old Masters, the Property of M. Emile Pacully, of Paris,* The Dowdeswell Galleries, London, 1901 (no. 8); Rotterdam, Museum Boymans van Bueningen, *Olieverfschelsen van Rubens,* Dec. 19, 1953-Feb. 14, 1954 (no. 73) cat. by Egbert Haverkamp-Begemann, pp. 85-86, repr. pl. 63); Bordeaux, *Flandres, Espagne, Portugal du XVe au XVIIe Siècle,* May 19-July 31, 1954 (no. 80) p. 83 in cat.; Brussels, Musées Royaux des Beaux-Arts de Belgique, *Le Siècle de Rubens,* Oct. 15-Dec. 12, 1965 (no. 225) pp. 215-216 in cat. by Leo van Puyvelde, repr.

Armand Hammer Collection Exhibitions: see pp. 17-18.
First exhibited Memphis, 1969. Not exhibited Kansas City; New Orleans; Columbus; Little Rock; San Francisco; Oklahoma City; San Diego; Los Angeles, 1974; Los Angeles, 1975; Moultrie.

Literature: Max Rooses, *L'Oeuvre de Pierre-Paul Rubens,* Antwerp, 1886-92, vol. 1, p. 73; P. Leprieur, "Ecoles du Nord," in *Collection Pacully,* Paris, 1900, p. 14, pl. 26; P. Leprieur and M. Rooses, in *Collection Emile Pacully, Tableaux anciens et modernes...dont la vente aura lieu Galerie Georges Petit...,* Paris, 1903, pp. 40, 41, 62, 63, no. 29, repr.; Max Rooses, "De Verzameling Pacully de Paris," *Onze Kunst* II 1903, pp. 121-122; Virgile Josz, "La Collection Emile Pacully," *Les Arts,* 2nd year, no. 16, (Apr. 1903), p. 35, repr. p. 36; "The Pacully Collection," *The Connoisseur,* May 1903, pp. 258, 259, repr.; N. Sentenac y Cantanas, *La pintura en Madrid desde sus origenes hasta el signo XIX,* Madrid, 1907, pp. 78 ff. (History and inventory of Pastrana collection); *Leo von Puyvelde, Les Esquisses de Rubens,* Basel, Holbein, 1940, p. 31, no. 7 (Engl. trans. London, 1947, p. 29); Egbert Haverkamp Begemann, "Rubens Schetsen," *Bulletin Museum Boymans Rotterdam,* vol. V, no. 1, Mar. 1954, p. 9, repr. p. 11; Victor H. Elbern, "Die Rubensteppiche des Kölner Domes, ihre Geschichte und ihre Stellung im Zyklus Triumph der Eucharistie," *Kölner Domblatt,* vol. X, 1955, pp. 74-75, repr. pl. 29; "Rubens Modello," *Bulletin of the Los Angeles County Museum of Art* (Annual Report 1968-69) XIX, 1968, pp. 12, 13, repr.; "La Chronique des Arts," *Gazette des Beaux-Arts,* 6th series, LXXIV, Dec. 1969, p. 4; "La Chronique des Arts," *Gazette des Beaux-Arts,* 6th series, LXXV, Feb. 1970, p. 58, no. 275, repr.; Nora de Poorter, *The Eucharist Series,* Corpus Rubenianum Ludwig Burchard, Part II, London, Miller & Heyden, 1978, vol. I, cat. 8b, pp. 116, 129-31, 216, 297-99, 305; vol. II, pl. 134-35.

Peter Paul Rubens
The Israelites Gathering Manna in the Desert, detail

About 1625 the Archduchess Isabella Clara Eugenia, daughter of Philip II of Spain and ruler of the Spanish Netherlands, commissioned Rubens to produce eleven huge paintings and several smaller ones to be used as cartoons (full-size patterns) for a series of tapestries glorifying the Eucharist which she wished to present to the Convent of the Descalzas Reales (Franciscan Clarissa Nuns) in Madrid. The subjects were: four Old Testament prefigurations of the New Testament Eucharist, one of which was the Israelites gathering manna in the desert; two of the Evangelists and Eucharistic teachers and defenders; and five Eucharistic triumphs. The first series of tapestries made in Brussels was sent to the convent in Madrid in July 1628. A second series is now in the Cathedral of Cologne. Other individual panels were woven.

In the preparation of the cartoons, Rubens first painted rough sketches in grisaille, then full-color sketches (*modelli*) which were enlarged by the master and his shop to the desired size of the tapestry. The first sketch for *The Israelites Gathering Manna in the Desert* is a panel (14.6 x 12.9 cm.) in the Musee Bonnat, Bayonne. In it, Moses is in the background of a composition with a strong movement from left to right. In preparing the Los Angeles *modello*, Rubens centralized the composition, confining it between Moses on the right and the woman with the child who turns toward center on the left. The woman is adapted from the woman with a jug in the Raphael *Fire in the Borgo*, in the Vatican; other elements in both the grisaille and the *modello* are related to a Rubens drawing in the Louvre (Lugt no. 1038, fig. 52; also repr. Elbern, 1958, fig. 12) after a Giulio Romano *Gathering of the Manna*. Employing Renaissance elements and classic compositional limits, Rubens has filled his stage with a dynamic movement and counter-movement of form, light and psychology not possible before the seventeenth century.

In 1648 Philip IV asked that the large cartoons and "other small paintings" for the Triumph of the Eucharist series be sent to Madrid. Many Rubens scholars have assumed that the sketches which were in the Royal collections of Spain in the late seventeenth century, including the Los Angeles sketch, were sent at that time and that the Los Angeles painting and other works from the Royal collections kept in the Pieza de las Furias were given after the death of Charles II in 1700 to Don Francisco Casimiro Pimentel, Count of Benavente, for himself and his successors. Nora de Poorter in her recent extensive study of the Eucharist series has concluded, however, that there is not adequate documentary evidence to prove that the *Gathering of the Manna* was ever in the Royal collections or that it was given to Pimentel. She does not suggest how or when it came to Spain, but she does feel that for some generations it was in the collection of the Dukes of Infantado, of the same family as the Counts of Benavente, since the first description of it in an inventory was in that of the Infantado collection of about 1800. From that time on the provenance is clear.

At some time, presumably towards the middle of the seventeenth century, the Los Angeles sketch was set into a larger panel and surrounded by a garland of flowers and fruits, first attributed to Jan Brueghel, then more precisely by Max Rooses (*Onze Kunst,* 1903) to Pieter Gysels (1621-1690). The *modello* with the garland is reproduced in the two Pacully sale catalogues, in *Les Arts,* 1903, and in de Poorter, 1978, II, pl. 135. The enlargement was removed and the panel was restored to its original size in 1938.

The large cartoon (canvas, 480.0 x 407.5 cm.) made from the Los Angeles *modello* was one of six cartoons sent in 1648 to Philip IV. He presented the six to Olivares, who placed them in his small family church at Loeches, near Madrid. They were removed by French troops during the Napoleonic invasions. Two became the property of the Louvre; four, including *The Israelites Gathering Manna in the Desert,* were sold in 1918 to the Duke of Westminster and in 1928 to John Ringling for the Ringling Museum in Sarasota, Florida (repr. William E. Suida, *Catalogue of Paintings in the John and Mable Ringling Museum of Art,* Sarasota, 1949, pp. 178-183). A copy of the Los Angeles *modello* is in the Museum of Doornik (Tournai). A School of Rubens drawing of the composition is in the Louvre (Lugt no. 1127).

K.D.

Jean-Honoré Fragonard 1732-1806
b. Grasse, France   *d.* Paris

7   *The Education of the Virgin,* 1748-52
Oil on panel 30.3 x 24.4 cm.

Collections: J.B.P. Lebrun, Paris; Fontaine, Paris; Charles T — , Paris; Camille Groult, Paris; Wildenstein & Co., Inc., New York; Mr. and Mrs. Henry R. Luce, New York.

Exhibitions: New Haven, Yale University Art Gallery, *Pictures Collected by Yale Alumni,* May 8-June 18, 1956 (no. 19), repr. in cat.

Armand Hammer Collection Exhibitions: see pp. 17-18.
First exhibited Memphis, 1969. Not exhibited San Diego; Los Angeles, 1974; Los Angeles, 1975; Moultrie.

Literature: *Catalogue d'objets rares et curieux, provenant du cabinet et fonds de marchandises de M. Lebrun par cessation de commerce,* sale catalogue, Galerie de M. Lebrun, Paris, Sept. 29, 1806, no. 150; Pierre de Nolhac, *J-H Fragonard,* Paris, 1906, p. 164; Georges Wildenstein, *The Paintings of Fragonard,* London, 1960, p. 195, no. 18, plate 1; Mahonri Sharp Young, "The Hammer Collection: Paintings," *Apollo,* vol. 95 (June 1972), p. 451.

Fragonard used the subject of Saint Anne teaching her daughter to read in at least three oil paintings. They include an unfinished picture in a private collection in Paris (Wildenstein, *Paintings of Fragonard,* no. 17, 90.0 x 72.0 cm., repr. in Louis Réau, *Fragonard,* Brussels, 1956, opp. p. 42), the present oil, which is almost certainly the preparatory sketch for the unfinished picture just mentioned, and a canvas now in the California Palace of the Legion of Honor, San Francisco (Wildenstein, no. 19, 82.0 x 116.0 cm.), probably cut down between 1793 and 1806. The Hammer oil sketch and a nearly identical black-and-brown wash drawing (39.0 x 28.0 cm.), were once the property of M. Camille Groult, Paris. The drawing, probably the original study for the Hammer oil sketch, was sold at the Charpentier sale in Paris, June 9-10, 1953, lot six, but its present whereabouts are not known. The Hammer study and the unfinished painting both show the Virgin looking up at her mother. The Charpentier drawing, in probably the first rendering of this pose, shows the Virgin lifting her face to her mother but with her eyes turned to the viewer. That the Virgin looks up rather than at the book makes an essential difference between this series and Fragonard's other versions of this subject. The Hammer sketch beautifully reveals the influence of Rembrandt on the young Fragonard, both in the strong handling of light and shadow and in the rich, golden palette.

M.E.

Francisco de Goya y Lucientes 1746-1828
b. Fuente de Todos, Spain   *d.* Bordeaux, France

8   *El Pelele,* ca. 1791
Oil on canvas 35.6 x 23.2 cm.

Collections: Doña Beatriz Sánchez de la Fuente de Lafora, Madrid; Don Juan de Lafora, Madrid;
M. Knoedler & Co., New York; Mr. and Mrs. Henry R. Luce, New York.

Exhibitions: Madrid, Sociedad Española de Amigos del Arte, *Bocetos y Estudias para Pinturas y
Esculturas,* May-June 1949 (no. 109), cat. by F. J. Sánchez-Canton; New Haven, Yale University Art
Gallery, *Pictures Collected by Yale Alumni,* May 8-June 18, 1956 (no. 29), repr. in cat.

Armand Hammer Collection Exhibitions: see pp. 17-18.
First exhibited Memphis, 1969. Not exhibited San Diego; Los Angeles, 1974; Los Angeles, 1975; Moultrie.

Literature: August L. Mayer, *Francisco de Goya,* Munich, 1923, p. 210, no. 570a (Engl. ed., London
and Toronto, 1924, p. 176, no. 570a); Valentín de Sambricio, *Tápices de Goya,* Patrimonio Nacional,
Archivo General del Palacio, Madrid, 1946, p. 273, no. 58a, plate CLXXXIV; Mahonri Sharp Young,
"The Hammer Collection: Paintings," *Apollo,* vol. 95 (June 1972), p. 451.

In 1776 Goya began a series of oil paintings of Spanish popular life to be used as cartoons for forty-six tapestries by the Real Fábrica de Tápices de Santa Bárbara in Madrid. The large cartoons are preserved in the Prado. *El Pelele* (Prado no. 802, 262.5 x 110.0 cm.), painted about 1791, was one of the last three cartoons delivered. The tapestry, today in the Palace of El Prado outside of Madrid, was executed in 1793.

There are two known *bocetos* for the Prado cartoon of *El Pelele,* one in the collection of Mrs. R. H. Kress (44.4 x 25.4 cm.), the other in this collection. The Hammer picture is presumably the first concept of the subject, with its freely sketched figures and the *pentimenti* in the straw man. Especially noticeable is the change in the position of the left foreleg. The group stands in an open space before a wall at the left and there is but the slightest indication of foliage at the right. The figures in the Kress picture are close to those in the Hammer picture;

the primary difference is in the development of a more airy and spacious background. Thus, the wall has receded and a large shrub has grown between it and the figure group to indicate the extension of space. In the Prado cartoon, the straw man has assumed a new and more limp position, the dresses and features of the four girls have been considerably elaborated, the wall has become a palace in the far distance, and delicate shrubbery creates a broad and deep landscape so that the straw man can be more effectively silhouetted against the sky.

The Hammer picture may well have been one of the *diez y seis bocetos pequeños de los tápices* listed in the inventory of the personal property of Francisco Goya in Madrid, and inherited by his son Javier Goya (inventory published in X. Desparmet Fitz-Gerald, *L'Oeuvre peint de Goya,* Paris, 1928-50, text vol. 1, pp. 53-54).

K.D.

Théodore Géricault 1791-1824
b. Rouen, France   *d.* Paris

9   *Portrait of a Gentleman,* ca. 1810-12
Oil on canvas 65.1 x 54.0 cm.
Signed, lower left: *T. G.*

Collections: Mr. Christi, Paris; Le Bohélec, Paris (sold Galerie Charpentier, Paris, June 16, 1955);
Drs. Fritz and Peter Nathan, Zurich.

Exhibitions: Winterthur, Switzerland, Kunstmuseum, *Théodore Géricault,* 1953 (no. 92); Los Angeles
County Museum of Art, Oct. 12-Dec. 12, 1971, Detroit Institute of Arts, Dec. 21, 1971-Feb. 27, 1972, and
Philadelphia Museum of Art, Mar. 30-May 14, 1972, *Géricault* (no. 3), repr. in cat.

Armand Hammer Collection Exhibitions: see pp. 17-18.
First exhibited Los Angeles, 1971-72. Not exhibited Los Angeles, 1974; Los Angeles, 1975; Moultrie; West
Palm Beach.

Literature: C. Clement, *Géricault, étude biographique et critique,* Paris, 1868 (3rd ed., enlarged, 1879),
p. 307, no. 121; F. H. Lem, "Géricault portraitiste," *L'Arte,* Jan.-June 1963, p. 68; Mahonri Sharp Young,
"The Hammer Collection: Paintings," *Apollo,* vol. 95 (June 1972), p. 451, repr. plate III in color p. 442.

Signed *T. G.* at the lower left, the picture was traditionally supposed to be a portrait of the composer F. A. Boïeldieu (1775-1834), although it does not bear any very pronounced resemblance to his known portraits. Because of its unusually tight and careful finish, the painting has, in Professor Lorenz Eitner's opinion, "no very evident connection with Géricault's characteristic personal manner." He has therefore put forward the ingenious hypothesis that it was "painted probably fairly early in Géricault's career, after the work of an artist of the previous generation." Eitner mentions other equally deceptive copies by Géricault, e.g., the copy after Hyacinthe Rigaud's *Portrait of the Mother of the Artist* (priv. coll., Paris). René Huyghe and Germain Bazin believe, on the other hand, that the unusual execution does not point to a copy but rather to the influence on Géricault of Antoine Jean Gros, whom he admired in his youth.

J.W.

Jean Baptiste Camille Corot 1796-1875
b. Paris *d.* Ville d'Avray, France

10   *Medieval Ruins,* ca. 1828-30
Oil on canvas, mounted on board 23.0 x 30.5 cm.
Stamped, lower right: *Vente Corot*
Verso: red wax seal of the Vente Corot

Collections: Vente Corot (Corot sale), Paris, 1875 (no. 329); Comte Armand Doria (sold Paris, May 5, 1899 (no. 108)); Mme Lazard, Paris; Mr. and Mrs. Eliot Hodgkin, London (sold Sotheby & Co., London, Apr. 29, 1964); Norton Simon, Los Angeles (sold Parke-Bernet Galleries, Inc., New York, May 5, 1971).

Exhibitions: Paris, Musée Jacquemart-André, *Le Second Empire,* 1957 (no. 62); Art Institute of Chicago, *Corot,* 1960 (no. 23); London, Marlborough Fine Art, Ltd., *Corot,* 1963 (no. 10); New York, Museum of Modern Art, May-July 1981; Omaha, Joslyn Art Museum, September-November, 1981; Los Angeles, Frederick S. Wight Art Galleries, January-February 1982; Chicago, Art Institute of Chicago, March-May 1982.

Armand Hammer Collection Exhibitions: see pp. 17-18.
First exhibited Oklahoma City. Not exhibited Los Angeles, 1975; Moultrie, Cincinnati.

Literature: Alfred Robaut, *L'Oeuvre de Corot,* Paris, 1905, vol. 2, p. 75, no. 212, repr.; *Impressionist and Modern Paintings, Drawings and Sculpture,* sale catalogue, Sotheby & Co., London, Apr. 29, 1964, no. 35A, repr.; *Highly Important 19th and 20th Century Paintings, Drawings & Sculpture from the Private Collection of Norton Simon,* sale catalogue, Parke-Bernet Galleries, Inc., New York, 1971, no. 2, repr.; Mahonri Sharp Young, "The Hammer Collection: Paintings," *Apollo,* vol. 95 (June 1972), p. 451.

Catalogued in the Vente Corot as "Pierrefonds, au pied du Château," this picture has been said by Alfred Robaut to be a view of Arques-la-Bataille. The latter site, near Dieppe, contains the ruins of an eleventh century fortress built by an uncle of William the Conqueror. The former, near Compiègne, was the site of a fourteenth century chateau, the remains of which were completely rebuilt by Viollet-le-Duc in the mid-nineteenth century at the order of Napoleon III. Robaut lists two views of Arques painted by Corot about the time of this sketch, and also three drawings and two paintings of Pierrefonds. Of the latter, three were executed in the 1840s and two in the 1860s. The present picture was probably painted between Corot's first two trips to Italy, that is, about 1828-30. It combines his interest in subjects observed on the spot with the luminism he had developed in the south. In this case, the evenness of the northern French light produces two large tonal areas, a light sky and a darker foreground, presaging the softness of Corot's late work and contrasting with the sharper illumination of his Italian pictures.

C.M.

Jean Baptiste Camille Corot 1796-1875

11   *Harvester under Trees,* ca. 1829
      Oil on canvas 40.1 x 30.5 cm.
      Stamped, lower left: *Vente Corot*

Collections: Vente Corot (Corot sale), Paris, 1875; M. Mauritz, Paris; Adrien Meunier, Paris; Galerie Daber, Paris.

Armand Hammer Collection Exhibitions: see pp. 17-18.
First exhibited New York City, 1968. Not exhibited San Diego; Los Angeles, 1975; Moultrie.

Literature: Alfred Robaut, *L'Oeuvre de Corot,* Paris, 1905, vol. 2, p. 74, no. 219 bis, vol. 4, p. 230, no. 323 bis (sketch by Robaut from posthumous sale catalogue, Paris, 1875); François Daulte, "Hammer en dix chefs-d'oeuvre," *Connaissance des arts,* Sept. 1970, pp. 82-83, repr. in color.

Executed at about the same time as the Hammer *Medieval Ruins* and in a similar, rapid style, this picture is considerably darker in tonality and for that reason more suggestive of the work of the Barbizon School. Only the harvester's white shirt and the light patch of sky relieve the rich greens and browns of the shadows. The serpentine wall connecting foreground and middleground and the diagonally recessive row of trees are unusual devices for Corot. They provide a somewhat more obvious pictorial scaffolding than one finds in the painter's later work. The subject is a scene of unposed action, also unusual for Corot.

C.M.

Jean Baptiste Camille Corot 1796-1875

12 *Distant View of Mantes Cathedral,* ca. 1855-60
    Oil on canvas 56.0 x 45.9 cm.
    Signed, lower left: *Corot*

Collections: M. Knoedler & Co., Paris (sold 1899); Galerie Georges Petit, Paris (sold Paris, Hôtel
Drouot, Apr. 27, 1933 (no. 49)); M. Damidot; Ferdinand Blumenthal, Paris; Léfèvre Gallery, London;
Count Pecci-Blunt, Rome; C. W. Boise, London.

Exhibitions: Paris, Galerie Georges Petit, *Exposition de Chefs-d'oeuvre de L'Ecole Française; vingt
peintres du XIXe siècle,* 1910 (no. 7); New York, M. Knoedler & Co., *The Landscape in French Painting,
XIXth-XXth Centuries,* 1910; Amsterdam, *Les Peintures Françaises aux XIXe et XXe Siècles,*
Apr.-May 1931.

Armand Hammer Collection Exhibitions: see pp. 17-18.
First exhibited New York City, 1968. Not exhibited Los Angeles, 1974; Los Angeles, 1975.

Literature: Alfred Robaut, *L'Oeuvre de Corot,* Paris, 1905, vol. 2, p. 264, no. 818, repr. p. 265; *Exposition
de Chefs-d'oeuvre de L'Ecole Française: vingt peintres du XIXe siècle,* catalogue, Galerie Georges Petit,
Paris, 1910, no. 7, repr. p. 103; Horace Shipp, *The French Masters,* London, 1931, repr. p. 112; *Art News,*
Apr. 8, 1933, repr. p. 8; *Gazette des beaux-arts,* Apr. 21, 1933, repr. p. 3; *Gazette des beaux-arts,*
May 5, 1933, p. 6; Germain Bazin, *Corot,* Paris, 1950, plate 92; Rodolphe Walter, "Jean Baptiste Corot
et la cathédrale restaurée," *Gazette des beaux-arts,* Apr. 1966, pp. 217-28, repr.; *Burlington Magazine,*
Apr. 1968, repr. p. vii, *Impressionist and Modern Paintings, Drawings and Sculpture — Various Owners,*
sale catalogue, Sotheby & Co., London, Apr. 24, 1968, no. 61, repr.; *Connoisseur,* Aug. 1968, repr. p. XIV;
Mahonri Sharp Young, "The Hammer Collection: Paintings," *Apollo,* vol. 95 (June 1972), p. 452,
repr. plate IV in color p. 445.

Mantes (Mantes-la-jolie), a small town east of
Paris notable for its magnificent church designed
by Pierre de Montreuil, architect of Notre Dame
at Paris, was painted many times by Corot
between the early 1840s and the 1860s. He
particularly favored its church and the bridge
across the Seine as motifs. The present picture
is not dissimilar to one in Reims made from a
slightly different viewpoint (Robaut, no. 1522),
although the composition is stronger by virtue
of the placement of the trees and the log lying
in the foreground. Two drawings in horizonal
format (Robaut, nos. 817, 1519) were apparently
made at the same spot. The disproportion in the
towers of the church has led Rodolphe Walter
to point out that the painting must have been
executed during the rebuilding of the south tower,
from 1859 to 1860. He convincingly suggests that
it dates to May 1859, when Corot was at nearby
Rosny. The tonality of the picture is somewhat
lighter and more even than is usual for Corot,
although he has been careful to add his usual
small touch of red to spark the blue-green of the
overall composition.

C.M.

Jean Baptiste Camille Corot 1796-1875

13   *Portrait of a Girl,* ca. 1860
      Oil on canvas 32.1 x 24.3 cm.
      Signed, upper right: *Corot*

Collections: Emile Bernheim, Paris; André Pacitti, Paris.

Armand Hammer Collection Exhibitions: see pp. 17-18.
First exhibited Kansas City, 1970. Not exhibited Los Angeles, 1975; Moultrie.

Literature: André Schoeller and Jean Dieterle, *Corot, deuxième supplément à "L'Oeuvre de Corot" par Alfred Robaut et Moreau-Nélaton,* Paris, 1956, no. 28; Mahonri Sharp Young, "The Hammer Collection: Paintings," *Apollo,* vol. 95 (June 1972), p. 451, repr. fig. 2 p. 443.

Degas was among the first to appreciate Corot's abilities as a figure painter, abilities that have generally gone unrecognized because of the popularity of the artist's landscapes. Toward the end of his life, Corot's figures became generalized into national or allegorical types, and individualized portraits such as this became increasingly rare. During the period when this picture was painted, Corot showed a marked predilection for a Leonardo-like figure characterized by a softly modeled face gazing outward and arms folded across each other. Corot's *Woman with the Pearl,* in the Louvre, is the best example of this type, and in fact the *Figures de Corot* catalogue (Louvre, 1962) suggests a relationship between the *Woman with the Pearl* and both the *Mona Lisa* and the *Belle Ferronière* of Leonardo. A portrait of a young woman in the Hirschland Collection represents an intermediate compositional step between the *Woman with the Pearl* and this picture.

C.M.

Jean Baptiste Camille Corot 1796-1875

14   *Morning,* 1865
      Oil on canvas 177.0 x 133.0 cm.
      Signed and dated, lower left: *Corot 1865*

Collections: M. Larrieu, Bordeaux; E. Secrétan, Paris (sold July 1, 1889 (no. 2)).

Exhibitions: Paris, *Salon de 1865* (no. 506), under the title *Le Matin*; Paris, Ecole Nationale des Beaux-Arts, 1875 (no. 148), lent by M. Larrieu; Paris, Arnold & Tripp, Feb. 1883.

Armand Hammer Collection Exhibitions: see pp. 17-18.
First exhibited Memphis, 1969. Not exhibited San Diego; Los Angeles, 1974; Moultrie.

Literature: Alfred Robaut, "La 'Bacchante' de Corot," *L'Art,* Feb. 18, 1883; Alfred Robaut, *L'Oeuvre de Corot,* Paris, 1905, vol. 3, no. 1635, repr. p. 145; Etienne Moreau-Nélaton, *Corot, raconté par lui-même,* Paris, 1924, vol. 2, fig. 191; Mahonri Sharp Young, "The Hammer Collection: Paintings," *Apollo,* vol. 95 (June 1972), p. 451.

Seeing this picture in the Salon of 1865, Paul Mantz wrote, "No landscape is as fresh, as tender, as bathed in the dawn as *Morning.*" In 1883, Alfred Robaut, decrying the small number of Corot paintings in French public collections, unsuccessfully demanded that the state allot one hundred thousand francs for its purchase. Robaut maintained that the composition had resulted from Corot's experience of an early morning in the country at Isigny and that a sketch made on the spot (Robaut, no. 846) was preparatory to it. The sketch, however, bears only slight resemblance to the final composition. Of unusual importance because of its size, *Morning* combines Corot's favorite motifs of classical figures and a dark but luminous setting seen against the light. The touch of red in the hair ribbon of the bacchante is typical of Corot. The darkening of the picture in the century since it was painted somewhat obscures the original transparency of the coloring. The work has been known variously as *Morning, Bacchante,* and *Bacchante Detaining an Amoretto.*

C.M.

Jean Baptiste Camille Corot 1796-1875

15   *Pleasures of Evening,* 1875
Oil on canvas 113.0 x 165.6 cm.
Signed and dated, lower left: *Corot 1875*

Collections: Jay Gould, New York; Edwin J. Gould, New York.

Exhibitions: Paris, *Salon de 1875* (no. 520); Paris, *Exposition Universelle Internationale de 1878*
(no. 201); New York, American Art Galleries, *Exhibition of the Works of Antoine Barye and also
Paintings by his Contemporaries and Friends, for the Benefit of the Barye Monument Fund,*
Nov. 15, 1889-Jan. 15, 1890 (no. 169), lent by Jay Gould.

Armand Hammer Collection Exhibitions: see pp. 17-18.
First exhibited New York City, 1968. Not exhibited Los Angeles, 1974; Los Angeles, 1975; Moultrie.

Literature: Ministère de l'Instruction Publique et des Beaux-Arts, *Salon de 1875, 92e exposition officielle,*
Paris, 1875, p. 77, no. 520; A. de la Fizelière, *Memento du salon de peinture, de gravure, et des sculptures
en 1875,* Paris 1875, pp. 32, 65, no. 520; Paul Leroi, "Salon de 1875, XV: Corot," *L'Art,* vol. 2 (1875),
p. 269, repr. in lithograph; *L'Exposition de l'oeuvre de Corot* (biographical note by P. Burty), Paris, 1875,
p. 31; Anatole de Montaiglon, "Salon de 1875," *Gazette des Beaux-arts,* ser. 2, vol. 12 (1875), p. 23; Henri
Dumesnil, *Corot, souvenirs intimes,* Paris, 1875, pp. 102, 130, no. 120; *L'Alliance des lettres et des arts,*
Apr. 1, 1875, repr., in pen drawing; *L'Univers illustre,* May 1, 1875, repr. in woodcut; Jules Claretie,
L'Art et les artistes français contemporains, Salon de 1875, Paris, 1876, p. 356; *Catalogue officiel de
l'Exposition Universelle Internationale de 1878 à Paris,* Paris, 1878, vol. 1, section 1 (Oeuvres d'Art),
p. 20, no. 201; *Exposition Universelle Internationale de Paris, 1878, le livre d'or des exposants,* Paris,
1878, p. 8; Jules Claretie, "C. Corot," *Peintres et sculpteurs contemporains,* ser. 1, Paris, 1882, pp. 97-120;
Jules-Antoine Castagnary, *Salons, 1857-1879,* Paris, 1892, vol. 2, p. 41; *Corot and Millet, with critical
essays by Gustave Geffroy and Arsène Alexandre,* London and New York, 1902, p. CXXVIII; Etienne
Moreau-Nélaton, *Histoire de Corot et de ses oeuvres,* Paris, 1905, pp. 342, 359, fig. 260; Alfred Robaut,
L'Oeuvre de Corot, Paris, 1905, vol. 1, p. 333, vol. 3, pp. 322-23, no. 2195, repr., vol. 4, pp. 170, 278, 378,
table p. 34; Etienne Moreau-Nélaton, *Corot, raconté par lui-même,* Paris, 1924, pp. 89, 105, fig. 258,
repr. p. 175; Germain Bazin, *Corot,* Paris, 1951 (2nd ed.), p. 115; Daniel Band-Bovy, *Corot,* Geneva, 1957,
p. 251; *Apollo,* May 1967, p. LXXXIV, repr.

Jules-Antoine Castagnary wrote of this picture
and the *Woodcutters,* both exhibited
posthumously in the Salon of 1875, that they
were "worthy of the most beautiful among their
predecessors." Among the last of Corot's
paintings, *Pleasures of Evening* repeats the
theme of an antique dance in the forest that
Corot had treated more than once before. Begun
at Courbron (a small town just east of Paris

where, toward the end of his life, Corot was in
the habit of visiting friends and working), the
picture was finished in Paris. Between the
inception and completion of this picture it was
sketched by Alfred Robaut (2195(A)). It is clear
from this sketch that Corot made several
changes after his return to Paris, apparently
reworking the figures in the group at right center
and adding the two figures at the left.

C.M.

Eugène Boudin 1824-1898
b. Honfleur, France   *d.* Deauville, France

16   *Sailing Ships in Port,* 1869
      Oil on canvas 45.1 x 64.3 cm.
      Signed and dated, lower left: *E. Boudin 1869*

Collection: Allard et Nöel, Paris (sold Palais Galliéra, Paris, May 30, 1967).

Armand Hammer Collection Exhibitions: see pp. 17-18.
First exhibited New York City, 1968. Not exhibited Los Angeles, 1974; Los Angeles, 1975; Moultrie.

Literature: *Deux importants tableaux par Eugène Boudin,* sale catalogue, Palais Galliéra, Paris, 1967, letter A, repr.; Mahonri Sharp Young, "The Hammer Collection: Paintings," *Apollo,* vol. 95 (June 1972), p. 452; Robert Schmit, *Eugène Boudin, 1824-1898,* Paris, 1973, vol. 1, p. 132, no. 467, repr.

Descended from seventeenth century Holland by way of eighteenth century Venetian *vedute,* Boudin's paintings contrast towering, broadly brushed skies with more precisely rendered, flickering groups of figures, ships, and buildings stretched out along the horizon. The precision of naturalistic observation and the narrow tonal range of grayed blue, green, and ocher, sparked with occasional accents of red, attracted the attention of the young Impressionists, most notably Monet. In 1869, the year of this picture, Boudin spoke of the "sun-drenched beaches and the stormy skies, and of the joy of painting them in the sea breezes."

C.M.

Eugène Boudin 1824-1898

17   *Quay at Camaret,* 1873
Oil on canvas 36.8 x 58.4 cm.
Signed and dated, lower left: *Boudin '73*
Inscribed, lower right: *Camaret*

Collections: Galerie Bernheim-Jeune, Paris; L. Bernard, Paris (sold Hôtel Drouot, Paris, May 11, 1901 (no. 7)); Théodore Révillon, Paris (sold Hôtel Drouot, Paris, May 8, 1924 (no. 11), repr. in cat.); Galerie Georges Petit, Paris; Galerie Schmit, Paris.

Armand Hammer Collection Exhibitions: see pp. 17-18.
First exhibited New York City, 1968. Not exhibited Los Angeles, 1974; Los Angeles, 1975.

Literature: Robert Schmit, *Eugène Boudin,* 1824-1898, Paris, 1973, vol. 1, p. 316, no. 893, repr.

In 1872 and 1873 Boudin worked at Camaret, in the extreme western tip of Brittany. This picture, somewhat stronger in its tonal contrasts than is common for Boudin, seems almost an illustration of Gustave Geffroy's statement that "Eugène Boudin is one of the immediate precursors of Impressionism.... He has perceived that opaque black does not exist, and that air is transparent. He observes the value that objects acquire when exposed to light, and how planes fall into place and lead to the horizon." Boudin himself, constantly conscious of the gap between his perceptions and his expressive powers, wrote, "Sometimes, as I walk sunken in melancholy, I look at the light inundating the earth, trembling on the water, playing on clothing, and I become faint when I realize how much genius is needed to grasp so many difficulties."

C.M.

Eugène Boudin 1824-1898

18   *Beach at Trouville,* ca. 1888-95
     Oil on canvas 18.6 x 32.7 cm.
     Signed, lower right: *a Mns Sonnerville* (sic) *Souvenir de E. Boudin*
     Inscribed, lower left: *Trouville*

Collections: De Sonneville, Bordeaux; William Hallsborough, Ltd., London; Lock Galleries, New York.

Armand Hammer Collection Exhibitions: see pp. 17-18.
First exhibited New York City, 1968. Not exhibited Los Angeles, 1974; Los Angeles, 1975; Moultrie.

Literature: *Art News,* Feb. 1967, repr. p. 53; Mahonri Sharp Young, "The Hammer Collection: Paintings," *Apollo,* vol. 95 (June 1972), p. 452, repr. fig. 3, p. 444. Robert Schmit, *Eugène Boudin, 1824-1898,* Paris, 1973, vol. 3, p. 392, no. 2346, repr.

The horizontal format of this sketch and the friezelike arrangement of people midway in the composition are characteristic of Boudin's beach scenes. This one was made at Trouville, one of his favorite haunts and among the most fashionable of the Second Empire resorts.

C.M.

Trouville

à m... Sommerville souvenir de E. Boudin.

Gustave Caillebotte 1848-1894
b. Paris   *d.* Gennevilliers, France

19   *Square in Argenteuil,* early 1880s
Oil on canvas 60.5 x 70.5 cm.
Signed, lower left: *G. Caillebotte*

Exhibition: Manila, National Museum of Manila, Oct. 1976.

Armand Hammer Collection Exhibitions: see pp. 17-18.
First exhibited New Orleans, 1970. Not exhibited Los Angeles, 1974; Los Angeles, 1975; Moultrie.

Literature: *Importants tableaux modernes,* sale catalogue, Palais Galliéra, Paris, June 17, 1970, no. 9;
Mahonri Sharp Young, "The Hammer Collection: Paintings," *Apollo,* vol. 95 (June 1972), p. 452.

Known principally as the collector who bequeathed the first great group of Impressionist pictures to the French state, Caillebotte was among the organizers of, and participants in, many of the original Impressionist exhibitions. As a painter, his vision was almost always advanced. He favored subjects from daily life in natural poses, although his execution was often tight and linear to the point of academicism. Caillebotte was at his best in his broadly conceived and freely brushed canvases, many of which — this painting is one — were executed at Argenteuil. This fresh and unexpected work probably dates from the early 1880s.

C.M.

Alfred Sisley 1839-1899
b. Paris, English parents   *d.* Moret-sur-Loing, France

20   *Timber Yard at Saint-Mammès,* 1880
Oil on canvas 55.6 x 72.9 cm.
Signed, lower right: *Sisley*

Collections: M. Feder, Paris; Galerie Durand-Ruel, Paris (purchased June 25, 1892); Paul Cassirer, Berlin; Galerie Europe, Brussels; sold Sotheby & Co., London, Nov. 29, 1967 (no. 28).

Exhibitions: Paris, Galerie Durand-Ruel, *Monet, Pissarro, Renoir et Sisley,* Apr. 1899 (no. 136); London, Grafton Gallery, *Paintings by Boudin, Sisley,* Jan.-Feb. 1905 (no. 303); Paris, Galerie Durand-Ruel, *Sisley,* June 1910 (no.71).

Armand Hammer Collection Exhibitions: see pp. 17-18.
First exhibited New York City, 1968. Not exhibited Los Angeles, 1974; Los Angeles, 1975.

Literature: Gustave Geffroy, *Sisley, Cahiers d'Aujour-d'hui,* no. 16, 1927, pp. 7-33, plate 28; Gotthard Jedlicka, *Sisley,* Bern, 1949, plate 37; François Daulte, *Alfred Sisley, catalogue raisonné de l'oeuvre peint,* Lausanne, 1959, no. 368, repr. p. 372; *Impressionist and Modern Paintings, Drawings and Sculpture,* sale catalogue, Sotheby & Co., London, 1967, no. 28, p. 47, repr. in color p. 46; *Burlington Magazine,* Nov. 1967, p.1, repr.; *Apollo,* Nov. 1967, p. CXVIII, repr.; *Art News,* Nov. 1967, p. 17, repr.; *Apollo,* June 1968, p. CII, repr.; *Connoisseur,* June 1968, p. XIV, repr.

Sisley was at his best in broad, close-valued, tonal painting. The typical commalike Impressionist facture tended to be disruptive of such painting, and Sisley used the technique most effectively when his strokes were of fairly uniform size and shape and his colors within one or two narrow ranges of tone — as in this picture. Saint-Mammès, to which Sisley eventually retired, was a small town on the banks of the Loing in the area southeast of Fontainebleau. François Daulte lists (nos. 369, 370, 372) at least three other compositons directly related to this and one (no. 371) of the same scene from the opposite direction.

C.M.

Claude Monet 1840-1926
b. Paris   *d.* Giverny, France

21   *View of Bordighera,* 1884
Oil on canvas 66.0 x 81.9 cm.
Signed and dated, lower left: *Claude Monet '84*

Collections: Galerie Durand-Ruel, Paris; M. Montaignac, Paris; James F. Sutton, New York (sold American Art Association at the Plaza Hotel, New York, Jan. 16-17, 1917 (no. 143)); James B. Hastings, New York; Nils B. Hersloff, Baltimore; Estate of Sigmund N. Hersloff, Baltimore (sold Parke-Bernet Galleries, Inc., New York, Oct. 28, 1970 (no. 5), p. 8 in cat., repr. in color).

Exhibitions: Paris, Galerie Georges Petit, *Claude Monet et A. Rodin,* 1889, lent by M. Montaignac; New York, Acquavella Galleries, Inc., Claude Monet Exhibition, Oct. 26-Nov. 28, 1976.

Armand Hammer Collection Exhibitions: see pp. 17-18.
First exhibited Little Rock, 1970-71. Not exhibited Los Angeles, 1974; Los Angeles, 1975.

Literature: Theodore Robinson, "Monet," in *Modern French Masters, a series of biographical and critical reviews by American artists with 37 wood engravings and 28 half-tone illustrations,* edited by John Charles Van Dyke, wood engraving by Michael Haider, New York, 1896, p. 170; *Apollo,* Oct. 1970, p. 141, repr.; *Burlington Magazine,* vol. 112 (Oct. 1970), p. lxxiv, repr.; *Art News,* Oct. 1970, repr.; L. Rossi Borlolatto, *Claude Monet,* Milan, 1972, pp. 105-106, no. 269, repr.; Mahonri Sharp Young, "The Hammer Collection: Paintings," *Apollo,* vol. 95 (June 1972), p. 452, repr. plate V in color p. 446.

During the 1880s, Monet's palette darkened. Combined with the discreteness and small size of Monet's brushstrokes and the intensity and value contrasts of his color, the darker palette tended to give his pictures a woolly texture that is especially noticeable in the Creuse and Belle Ile paintings. This picture contrasts that roughness with an atmospheric distance and is therefore somewhat less surface-oriented than the similar painting in Chicago. Monet had been attracted to the south of France on a visit there with Renoir in 1883, and in January of 1884 he returned to paint first at Bordighera, on the Italian Riviera, and then at Menton.

C.M.

Camille Pissarro 1830-1903
b. Saint-Thomas, Virgin Islands   *d.* Paris

22   *Boulevard Montmartre, Mardi Gras,* 1897
Oil on canvas 63.5 x 80.0 cm.
Signed and dated, lower left: *C. Pissarro '97*

Collections: Maurice Barret-Décap, Paris; Mr. and Mrs. Henry R. Luce, New York; Marlborough Alte und Moderne Kunst, Zurich; Norton Simon, Los Angeles (sold Parke-Bernet Galleries, Inc., New York, May 5, 1971 (no. 24)).

Exhibitions: Paris, Galerie Durand-Ruel, *C. Pissarro,* 1898 (no. 20); Paris, Galerie Durand-Ruel, *Tableaux, Pastels et Gouaches de C. Pissarro,* 1921 (no. 9); Paris, Galerie Durand-Ruel, *C. Pissarro,* 1928 (no. 78); New Haven, Yale University Art Gallery, *Paintings, Drawings, and Sculpture Collected by Yale Alumni,* May 19-June 26, 1960 (no. 58), repr. in cat.; New York, Wildenstein & Co., Inc., *C. Pissarro,* Mar. 25-May 1, 1965 (no. 65), repr. in cat.; Pittsburgh, Carnegie Institute, The Sarah Scaife Gallery of the Museum of Art, *Inaugural Celebration Exhibition,* Oct. 26-Dec. 9, 1974; London, Hayward Gallery, *Camille Pissarro,* Oct. 30, 1980-Jan. 11, 1981 (no. 78); Paris, Grand Palais, *Camille Pissarro,* Jan. 30-Apr. 27, 1981 (no. 78); Boston, Museum of Fine Arts, *Camille Pissarro,* May 19-Aug. 9, 1981 (no. 78), repr. in cat.

Armand Hammer Collection Exhibitions: see pp. 17-18.
First exhibited Oklahoma City, 1971. Not exhibited Los Angeles, 1974; Los Angeles, 1975; Washington, D.C., 1980; West Palm Beach; Cincinnati.

Literature: Ludovic-Rodo Pissarro and Lionello Venturi, *Camille Pissarro, son art — son oeuvre,* Paris, 1939, no. 995, vol. 2, plate 200; *Highly Important 19th and 20th Century Paintings, Drawings & Sculpture from the Private Collection of Norton Simon,* sale catalogue, Parke-Bernet Galleries, Inc., New York, 1971, p. 40, no. 24, repr. in color.

Pissarro produced several paintings of the Boulevard Montmartre in 1897 (Pissarro and Venturi, nos. 986-998), three of which (Pissarro and Venturi, nos. 995-997) seem to represent successive stages of a Lenten parade. While the three are surely related, two, including this one, are catalogued by Pissarro and Venturi as Mardi Gras scenes and the third as a Mi-Carême. This picture is characteristic of Pissarro's late city scenes, particularly views of Paris, seen at sharp downward angles. Characteristic, too, is the blond tonality and the obvious feathery or calligraphic brushwork Pissarro used toward the end of his life. Partly because of the nature of the subject, this picture has somewhat more color than some other Paris views by the artist.

C.M.

Pierre-Auguste Renoir 1841-1919
b. Limoges, France   *d.* Cagnes, France

23   *Grape Pickers at Lunch,* ca. 1888
Oil on canvas 55.5 x 46.4 cm.
Signed, lower left: *Renoir*

Collections: Arsène Alexandre, Paris; Rosenberg & Stiebel, New York.

Exhibition: London, Royal Academy of Arts, *Post-Impressionism,* 1979-80.

Armand Hammer Collection Exhibitions: see pp. 17-18.
First exhibited Memphis, 1969. Not exhibited Houston; Moultrie.

Literature: Sale catalogue, Galerie Georges Petit, Paris, May 1903, no. 54; François Daulte, *Auguste Renoir: catalogue raisonné de l'oeuvre peint,* Lausanne, 1971, vol. 1, no. 467, repr., as Renoir, 1884.

This picture, with its sharp contrasts of hue and its carefully drawn forms, is a product of the mid-1880s — a period of experimentation and reevaluation for Renoir. He had earlier questioned the validity of recording purely visual impressions, and, after studying the Raphael paintings in Rome and the ancient frescoes from Pompeii in the Naples Museum during an Italian trip in 1881-82, Renoir sought to reassess the importance of drawing, line, modeled form, and compositional reorganization of nature. He even questioned the soundness of painting in the open air directly from nature as opposed to composing in the studio. Like Cézanne, but in his own way, he devoted himself at this time to establishing harmony between Impressionism and the "art of the museums."

The *Grape Pickers at Lunch* is a product of Renoir's exploration of some of these concepts. Instead of his usual soft brushwork, he uses smaller, sharper, more graphic strokes, which define and model the figures. Instead of merging his figures with the landscape, as in the Impressionist works of the 1870s, he arranges his figures to form a closed concentric group; this establishes a real but limited foreground space, reminiscent of Renaissance "stagelike" space, to which the landscape forms a backdrop.

The probability that the painting is a studio composition is reinforced by the reappearance of the girl with the basket on her back, who had been used by Renoir in the *Mussel Gatherers at Berneval,* painted in 1879 and shown in the Salon of 1880. The three girls in the foreground are said to be the daughters of Paul Alexis.

C.M.

Pierre-Auguste Renoir 1841-1919

24 *Antibes,* 1888
  Oil on canvas 64.8 x 81.3 cm.
  Signed and dated, lower right: *Renoir '88*

Collections: Galerie Durand-Ruel, Paris, 1910; Baroness von Brenin, Berlin, 1931; Parke-Bernet Galleries, Inc., New York (sold Feb. 25, 1970 (no. 21)).

Exhibitions: Paris, Galerie Durand-Ruel, *Exposition de Tableaux par Renoir,* Apr. 27-May 15, 1912 (no. 5); Akron Art Institute, 1947; Milwaukee Art Institute, *Masters of Impressionism,* 1948 (no. 38); Art Institute of Chicago, *Renoir Exhibition,* Jan. 30-Apr. 1, 1973.

Armand Hammer Collection Exhibitions: see pp. 17-18.
First exhibited Kansas City, 1970. Not exhibited Kiev; Minsk; Riga; Odessa; Los Angeles, 1974; Los Angeles, 1975.

Literature: *Highly Important Impressionist, Post-Impressionist & Modern Paintings and Drawings,* sale catalogue, Parke-Bernet Galleries, Inc., New York, 1970, no. 21, repr. in color; Mahonri Sharp Young, "The Hammer Collection: Paintings," *Apollo,* vol. 95 (June 1972), p. 452.

During the 1880s, Renoir's efforts to restudy his draftsmanship resulted in a hard and carefully outlined figure style usually at variance with the continued softness of his backgrounds. Only in the nonfigural subjects, such as this view of Antibes, did he maintain and develop his feathery brush style, suppressing contour to an extent that makes the subjects of these pictures seem almost to evaporate. A similar composition is recorded in the collection of Sir Simon and Lady Marks.

C.M.

Pierre-Auguste Renoir 1841-1919

25 *Two Girls Reading,* 1890-91
Oil on canvas 55.9 x 47.2 cm.
Signed, lower right: *Renoir*

Collections: Galerie Durand-Ruel, Paris, purchased 1895 from Renoir; H. O. Niethke Gallery,
Vienna, purchased 1912; Dr. Herman Eissler, Vienna; Hugo Moser, Heemstede; Mrs. Maria Moser,
New York; Dr. and Mrs. Armand Hammer, Los Angeles; Los Angeles County Museum of Art, gift of
Dr. and Mrs. Armand Hammer, 1968.

Exhibitions: Zurich, Kunsthaus, 1933; Haarlem, Frans Hals Museum, 1936; Baltimore Museum of Art,
summer, 1939; New York, Wildenstein & Co., Inc., *Renoir,* Apr. 8-May 10, 1958 (no. 53), p. 67 in cat.,
repr.; New York, Metropolitan Museum of Art, 1959-67; New York, Wildenstein & Co., Inc., *Renoir,*
Mar. 27-May 3, 1969 (no. 77); Manila, National Museum of Manila, Oct. 1976.

Armand Hammer Collection Exhibitions: see pp. 17-18.
First exhibited New York City, 1968. Not exhibited Columbus; Little Rock; Los Angeles, 1975; Moultrie.

Literature: Baltimore Museum of Art, *Quarterly,* July 1, 1939, p. 8, repr.; Los Angeles County Museum
of Art, *Annual Report,* 1968-69, pp. 18-19, repr.; Alfred Weiner, "Renoir's Daimon," *Arts Magazine,*
Apr. 1969, p. 40, repr.; *Gazette des beaux-arts,* Feb. 1970, supplement, p. 87, repr.; Mahonri Sharp Young,
"The Hammer Collection: Paintings," *Apollo,* vol. 95 (June 1972), p. 452, repr. fig. 4, p. 447.

This gentle and slightly nostalgic subject is of
the kind that most appealed to Renoir and that
he was best able to execute successfully. The
consistency of the brushwork and the warmth
of color help unify the composition, and the
painting shows the renewed softness of Renoir's
work toward the end of the century. The girl at
the left is said to be Julie Manet, daughter of
Berthe Morisot and Eugène Manet, while the
one at the right is possibly Julie's cousin Paule
Gobillard. A less satisfying variation of this
composition is recorded in a Scottish private
collection (repr. *Scottish Art Review,* vol. 4, no. 4
(1953), p. 19); there is also a three-quarter-length
variation of a similar subject (repr. *Beaux-Arts*
Feb. 22, 1935, p. 4).

C.M.

Berthe Morisot 1841-1895
b. Bourges, France   *d.* Paris

26   *Jeune Fille au Chien (Young Girl with a Dog),* ca. 1887 (Paule Gobillard — Niece of Berthe Morisot)
Oil on canvas 72.8 x 60.1 cm.

Collections: Paule Gobillard, Quimperlé; Morisot family, Paris.

Exhibitions: Paris, Galerie Durand-Ruel, *Berthe Morisot,* Mar. 1896 (no. 29); Paris, Galerie Marcel Bernheim, *Berthe Morisot,* June-July 1922 (no. 27); Copenhagen, Ny Carlsberg Glyptotek, *Berthe Morisot,* Aug.-Sept. 1949 (no. 37); Musée de Dieppe, *Exposition Berthe Morisot,* July-Sept. 1957 (no. 38); New York, Wildenstein & Co., Inc., *Berthe Morisot,* Nov. 1960 (no. 45).

Armand Hammer Collection Exhibitions: see pp. 17-18.
First exhibited Atlanta, 1977-78. Not exhibited Moultrie.

Literature: M.L. Bataille and G. Wildenstein, *Berthe Morisot,* "Les Beaux-Arts," Editions d'étude et documents, Paris, 1961, p. 36, no. 209, repr. plate 63, as painted in 1887.

Paule Gobillard and her younger sister were daughters of Berthe Morisot's sister and, like Morisot's own daughter, Julie, were among her favorite models. Berthe Morisot had a warm, maternal feeling for children and young people. This, coupled with her keen intelligence, produced some of the most sympathetic portraits of the Impressionist School. Hers was an essentially feminine vision and, indeed, most of her subjects were women. Denis Rouart, her grandson, described the sitters who most appealed to her: beloved friends and family, frequent guests, and favorite children.

The Hammer portrait, of about 1887, is one of the last pictures she painted in the style of her highly successful first period (1878-88). In this decade, more assured of herself as a painter than at any other time, Berthe Morisot brought together the two main influences of her life. On the one hand, she explored the lessons of the 1860s learned from her friend Corot. At the age of sixty-four, he had inspired her to see the effects of natural light and atmosphere. On the other hand, since meeting in 1868 her future brother-in-law, Edouard Manet, she had been increasingly liberated by his unconventional approach to painting. It was his freedom of brushwork and his volatile spirit that attracted her to his style and to him. In this period, there are no preliminary sketches or even superficial outlines on the canvas; there are only bold, irregular, and rapid strokes of paint. Like most Impressionists, Berthe Morisot worked with speed and spontaneity, directly on canvas. Rouart described her particular technique as "brushwork like fireworks." His phrase is brilliantly exemplified by the Hammer picture. Within a year of this picture, Berthe Morisot's style was to change radically. She became interested in mass and form. The explosive slashes of color typical of her work until 1888 gave way to long, continuous lines enclosing smooth, serene shapes.

M.E.

Paul Cézanne 1839-1906
b. Aix-en-Provence, France   *d.* Aix-en-Provence

27   *Boy Resting,* ca. 1885
Oil on canvas 54.5 x 65.5 cm.

Collections: Ambroise Vollard, Paris; Galerie Bernheim-Jeune, Paris; Galerie Thannhauser, Lucerne;
Josef Stransky, New York; Estate of Josef Stransky (on loan to the Worcester Art Museum, Worcester,
Mass., June 1, 1932-Mar. 9, 1936); Wildenstein & Co., Inc., New York; Arnold Kirkeby, New York (sold
Parke-Bernet Galleries, Inc., New York, No. 19, 1958 (no. 16)); Mrs. Arnold Kirkeby, Los Angeles.

Exhibitions: Paris, Galerie Bernheim-Jeune, *Retrospective Paul Cézanne,* June 1-30, 1926 (no. 5);
New York, Museum of Modern Art, *1st Loan Exhibition,* Nov. 1929 (no. 13); Art Institute of Chicago,
A Century of Progress, June 1-Nov. 1, 1933 (no. 318A); Worcester, Mass., Worchester Art Museum,
The Loan Exhibition of the New Museum Building, 1933-34; San Francisco, California Palace of the
Legion of Honor, *French Painting from the 15th Century to the Present Day,* June 8-July 8, 1934
(no. 65); Kansas City, William Rockhill Nelson Gallery of Art, *Nineteenth Century French Painting,*
Mar. 15-Apr. 12, 1936; London, Wildenstein & Co., Ltd., *Collection of a Collector, Modern Painting from
Ingres to Matisse, The Private Collection of the Late Josef Stransky,* July 1936 (no. 18); Toledo, Ohio,
Toledo Museum of Art, *Cézanne, Gauguin,* Nov. 1-Dec. 13, 1936 (no. 29); San Francisco Museum of Art,
Paul Cézanne, Sept. 1-Oct. 4, 1937 (no. 16), repr. in cat.; London, Wildenstein & Co., Ltd., *Homage to
Paul Cézanne,* July 1939 (no. 30); New Haven, Yale University Art Gallery, *Cézanne and the French
Tradition,* Jan. 29-Feb. 18, 1945; Cincinnati Art Museum, *Paintings by Paul Cézanne,* Feb. 5-Mar. 9, 1947
(no. 4); New York, Wildenstein & Co., Inc., *A Loan Exhibition of Paul Cézanne for the Benefit of the
New York Infirmary,* Mar. 27-Apr. 26, 1947 (no. 19); Los Angeles, Art Galleries, University of California,
California Collects: North and South, Jan. 20-Feb. 23, 1958 (no. 29), repr. in cat.; Tokyo, National
Museum of Western Art, Mar. 20-Apr. 19, 1974, Kyoto, Municipal Museum, June 1-July 17, 1974,
Fukuoka, Prefectural Cultural Center Museum, July 24-Aug. 18, 1974, *Cézanne Exhibition.*

Armand Hammer Collection Exhibitions: see pp. 17-18.
First exhibited Oklahoma City, 1971. Not exhibited Los Angeles, 1974; Los Angeles, 1975.

Paul Cézanne
Boy Resting, detail

Literature: *Kunst und Kunstler,* vol. 24 (1926), pp. 448-49; *International Studio,* Nov. 1929, p. 66, repr.; Eugenio d'Ors, *Paul Cézanne,* Paris, 1930, p. 25, repr., table VI; Ralph Flint, "The Private Collection of Josef Stransky," *Art News,* May 16, 1931, p. 8, repr.; Perry B. Cott, "The Stransky Collection of Modern Art," *Bulletin of the Worcester Art Museum,* Winter, 1933, p. 157; Nina Iavorskaïa, *Paul Cézanne,* Milan, 1935, plate VI; *Art Digest,* Apr. 1, 1936, p. 5, repr.; *Parnassus,* Dec. 1936, p. 26, repr.; Maurice Raynal, *Cézanne,* New York, 1936, plate 51; Lionello Venturi, *Cézanne, son art — son oeuvre,* Paris, 1936, vol. 1, p. 150, no. 391, vol. 2, no. 391, plate 107; Ambroise Vollard, *Paul Cézanne, His Life and Art* (trans. Harold L. Van Doren), New York, 1937, plate 9; *Art News,* Oct. 1958, p. 41, repr.; "Kirkeby Collection at Auction," *Arts,* Nov. 1958, p. 27, repr.; *Connoisseur,* Nov. 1958, p. 124, repr.; *Connoisseur,* Jan. 1959, p. 254, repr.; *Apollo,* June 1959, p. 215, repr.; Robert Melville, "Exhibitions," *Architectural Review,* Aug. 1959, pp. 131-33, repr.; Mark Roskill, *Van Gogh, Gauguin, and the Impressionist Circle,* London, 1970, p. 231, plate 179; M. Brion, *Paul Cézanne,* Milan, 1971, p. 77, repr.; Elie Faure, *Cézanne,* Paris, n.d., plate 7.

The subject of this picture of a reclining clothed figure, unique in Cézanne's oeuvre, was considered by Ambroise Vollard to be the artist's son, Paul. The composition exemplifies the artist's struggle to reconcile pictorial and naturalistic scale and effect. The broad rectilinear paint areas at the top of the canvas were clearly conceived as flat elements directly related to the size and shape of that canvas. Their two-dimensional strength creates a pictorial pressure that jeopardizes the human identity of the figure, makes its location in depth ambiguous, and mitigates its three-dimensionality. That Cézanne could explore such complex problems without sacrificing the quality of his art is an index of his genius.

C.M.

Henri Fantin-Latour 1836-1904
b. Grenoble, France   *d.* Buré, France

28   *Peonies in a Blue and White Vase,* 1872
Oil on canvas 60.8 x 49.9 cm.
Signed and dated, upper right: *Fantin 1872*

Collections: Dr. J. van Alphen-Carp, the Netherlands; E. J. van Wisselingh & Co., Amsterdam; M. L. de Boer, Amsterdam.

Armand Hammer Collection Exhibitions: see pp. 17-18.
First exhibited New York City, 1968.

Literature: Mme Fantin-Latour, *Catalogue de l'oeuvre complète de Fantin-Latour,* Paris, 1911, no. 616; *Art Journal,* Fall, 1968, p. LIV, repr.; *Connoisseur,* Nov. 1968, p. 11 repr.; François Daulte, "Hammer en dix chefs-d'oeuvre," *Connaissance des arts,* Sept. 1970, p. 83, repr.

Fantin is most widely known for his flower pictures, in the best of which white predominates against a cool, hued background. Seen in isolation, the flowers in these paintings project in astonishing relief and tactility. This heightened sense of reality is partly due to the apparent lack of atmosphere in the flower pieces. Perhaps none of these paintings illustrates as well as this one Jacques-Emile Blanche's observation that "Fantin studied each flower, each petal, its grain, its tissue as if it were a human face.... It is an individual flower and not simply one of a type.... Some canvases are worthy of Chardin."

C.M.

Henri Fantin-Latour 1836-1904

29   *Portrait of Miss Edith Crowe,* 1874
      Oil on canvas 73.0 x 59.2 cm.
      Signed and dated, upper left: *Fantin '74*

Collections: Mme Paul Paix; Mrs. D. Bergen-Hayn; Galerie l'Oeil, Paris.

Exhibitions: Paris, *Salon de 1875* (no. 783); Paris, Ecole Nationale des Beaux-Arts, *Exposition de l'Oeuvre de Fantin-Latour,* May-June 1906 (no. 41); Amsterdam, Stedelijk Museum.

Armand Hammer Collection Exhibitions: see pp. 17-18.
First exhibited Memphis, 1969. Not exhibited San Diego; Los Angeles, 1974; Los Angeles, 1975; Moultrie.

Literature: Ministère de l'Instruction Publique et des Beaux-Arts, *Salon de 1875, 92e exposition officielle,* Paris, 1875, p. 115, no. 783, Paul Leroi, *L'Art, Salon de 1875,* Paris, 1875, vol. 1, p. 137, no. 783; Adolpe Julien, *Fantin-Latour, sa vie et ses amitiés,* Paris, 1909, p. 199; Mme Fantin-Latour, *Catalogue de l'oeuvre complète de Fantin-Latour,* Paris 1911, p. 81, no. 739; *Connoisseur,* Nov. 1970, p. 210, repr.; Mahonri Sharp Young, "The Hammer Collection: Paintings," *Apollo,* vol. 95 (June 1972), p. 452.

This picture was exhibited as "Portrait of Mlle E. C — " in the Salon of 1875 along with Fantin's superb double portrait of his English friends and patrons, Mr. and Mrs. Edwin Edwards, to whom he had been introduced by Whistler. Miss Crowe was presumably a friend of the Edwardses, or of someone whom they had introduced to Fantin. It has been reported that she was the youngest of a large family who lived in Paris. Apparently, her house was like a salon for many of the artists of that time. Broader in technique than Fantin's flower pieces, this picture is not yet as free as the allegories and Wagnerian paintings. The placement of the figure against an unmodulated dark ground suggests what Fantin may owe to Manet, although the head is developed in a more traditional chiaroscuro. Speaking of another of Fantin's portraits, Zola noted that "each of his canvases is an act of conscience. He excels at painting figures in the atmosphere in which they live, in giving them a warmth and supple life; it is that which means that, despite the restraining frame in which it is enclosed, this hardly seems to be a portrait, it is nothing less than a thing apart, very elevated."

                                                                    C.M.

90

Henri Fantin-Latour 1836-1904

30 *Roses,* 1884
Oil on canvas 66.2 x 57.7 cm.
Signed and dated, upper left: *Fantin '84*

Collections: Mrs. Edwards, London; Miss R. Bryant, London; Arthur Tooth & Sons, Ltd., London;
Mrs. Hazel C. Boise, London (sold Sotheby & Co., London, Apr. 26, 1967 (no. 7)).

Exhibitions: Musée de Grenoble, *Exposition du Centenaire de la Naissance de Fantin-Latour,*
Aug.-Oct. 1936 (no. 145); London, Arthur Tooth & Sons, Ltd., *French Pictures from Private Collections,*
June 1949 (no. 19).

Armand Hammer Collection Exhibitions: see pp. 17-18.
First exhibited New York City, 1968. Not exhibited Los Angeles, 1974; Los Angeles, 1975; Moultrie.

Literature: Mme Fantin-Latour, *Catalogue de l'oeuvre complète de Fantin-Latour,* Paris, 1911, no. 1167;
Burlington Magazine, Apr. 1967, p. XVI, repr.; *Connoisseur,* Apr. 1967, p. XCIII, repr.; *Impressionist
and Modern Paintings and Sculpture,* sale catalogue, Sotheby & Co., London, 1967, p. 15, no. 7, repr. p. 14;
Mahonri Sharp Young, "The Hammer Collection: Paintings," *Apollo,* vol. 95 (June 1972), p. 452.

The Mrs. Edwards who originally owned this picture is presumably Mrs. Edwin Edwards, wife of Fantin's English friend and patron. Whereas Fantin's portraits and genre subjects were favored in France, his flower pictures were particularly popular in England. His submissions to the Royal Academy between 1862 and 1900 consisted almost entirely of such subjects, many of which had poetic titles such as *Here Without a Thorn, the Rose.* Although this picture seems originally to have been called simply *Roses,* it has been known as *All the Roses of the Garden,* probably because of Mme Fantin-Latour's description of it in her catalogue. *Roses* is a "poetic," close-valued painting, somewhat more broadly brushed than the Hammer *Peonies.* The pastel pinks and yellows mediate between the white highlights and the deep red and dark greens, softening the picture's general appearance. This atmospheric facture is particularly appropriate in view of the literary associations roses seem regularly to have evoked in Fantin.

C.M.

Edgar Degas 1834-1917
b. Paris   *d.* Paris

31   *Three Dancers in Yellow Skirts,* ca. 1891
     Oil on canvas 81.3 x 65.1 cm.
     Signed, lower right: *Degas*

Collections: Atelier Degas (sold Galerie Georges Petit, Paris, first sale, May 6-8, 1918 (no. 92), repr. in cat.); MM. Nunès and Fiquet, Paris; F.R. (sold Paris, Mar. 8, 1930 (no. 74)); sold Galerie René Drouet, Paris; Erwin Swann, Pennsylvania (sold Sotheby & Co., London, Dec. 10, 1969 (no. 20)).

Exhibition: New York, Gallery of Modern Art, *The Pleasure of the Eye — The Collection of Caroline and Erwin Swann,* 1964-65 (no. 9).

Armand Hammer Collection Exhibitions: see pp. 17-18.
First exhibited Washington, D.C., 1970. Not exhibited Los Angeles, 1974; Los Angeles, 1975.

Literature: *Catalogue des tableaux, pastels et dessins par Edgar Degas,* catalogue of first sale, Galerie Georges Petit, Paris, 1918, p. 51, no. 92, repr.; *Catalogue de la Vente F. R.,* sale catalogue, Hôtel Drouot, Paris, 1930, 2nd part, no. 74, p. 20, repr.; P. A. Lemoisne, *Degas et son oeuvre,* Paris, 1947, vol. 3, p. 636, no. 1100, repr.; *Impressionist and Modern Paintings,* sale catalogue, Sotheby & Co., London, 1969, no. 20, repr. in color; Mahonri Sharp Young, "The Hammer Collection: Paintings," *Apollo,* vol. 95 (June 1972), p. 452, repr. plate VII in color p. 449.

This picture is similar in size and conception to the Louvre's *Dancers in Blue,* which is closely related to the Metropolitan Museum's *Dancers in Red and Green.* The Louvre picture, in blue-green-purple and the Hammer picture, in red-yellow-orange seem, in fact, to be coloristic variations on the same theme. Degas experimented at this time with broadly stippled backgrounds in other pictures, notably in his studies of dancers (L. 975) and of bathers (L. 1104). The placement of the figures suggests the same or similar poses seen from different angles of vision, a device increasingly exploited by Degas. Along with his interest in different poses arranged sequentially, the resulting photocinematic effect certainly reflects Degas' knowledge of early experiments in motion photography. This effect is enhanced by the suggestion of an unstable equilibrium resulting from the eccentric arrangement of the figures. The entire composition is stabilized by Degas' manipulation of his hues and their values.

C.M.

Henri de Toulouse-Lautrec 1864-1901
b. Albi, France   *d.* Malromé, France

32   *In the Salon,* 1894
Oil on cardboard 60.6 x 40 cm.
Signed, lower left: *HT-Lautrec*

Collections: Octave Maus, Brussels; Tetze-Lund, Copenhagen; J. K. Thannhauser, New York; Paul Rosenberg, New York (sold Sotheby & Co., London, Nov. 7, 1962 (no. 85)); Galerie Beyeler, Basel.

Exhibitions: Paris, Galerie Manzi et Joyant, *Toulouse-Lautrec,* 1896; Brussels, *Exposition Toulouse-Lautrec,* organized by La Libre Esthétique, Mar. 1902; Paris, Galerie Manzi et Joyant, *Exposition Retrospective de L'Oeuvre de H. Toulouse-Lautrec,* June 15-July 11, 1914 (no. 39); Liège, Musée des Beaux Arts, 1978; Chicago, The Art Institute of Chicago, *Toulouse-Lautrec: Paintings,* Oct. 6-Dec. 2, 1979, (no. 74).

Armand Hammer Collection Exhibitions: see pp. 17-18.
First exhibited New York City, 1968. Not exhibited Los Angeles, 1974; Los Angeles, 1975; Paris; Houston; Moultrie.

Literature: Maurice Joyant, *Henri de Toulouse-Lautrec,* Paris, 1926, p. 286; Gotthard Jedlicka, *Henri de Toulouse-Lautrec,* Erlenbach-Zurich, 1943, p. 321, repr. opp. p. 218; Francis Jourdin and Jean Adhémar, *Toulouse-Lautrec,* Paris, 1952, plate 84; *Impressionist and Modern Paintings, Drawings and Sculpture,* sale catalogue, Sotheby & Co., London, 1962, no. 85, repr. in color; P. Huisman and M. G. Dortu, *Lautrec by Lautrec,* New York, 1964, pp. 130-131, repr. in color; *Apollo,* Sept. 1966, p. LXXV, repr.; "On the Market," *Apollo,* Nov. 1968, p. 395, repr.; François Daulte, "Hammer en dix chefs-d'oeuvre," *Connaissance des arts,* Sept. 1970, p. 79, repr.; *Connoisseur,* Nov. 1970, p. 210, repr.

From 1892 until 1895, Toulouse-Lautrec produced a series of pictures of prostitutes and bordello scenes. The summation of this work was the large canvas, *In the Salon,* painted in 1894 and now in the museum at Albi. There is a pastel version of the complete composition in the same museum and a large group of related studies, of which this picture is one. Presumably also executed in 1894, it represents the same two women who are seated at the left rear center of the Albi painting. According to Maurice Joyant, the woman seen in profile is the Rolande of several of the other studies. In transferring the figures to the larger work, Lautrec has altered only the position of the arms. The technique of this study is much broader than that of the finished picture, and its color is worked out in terms of close-valued, close-hued, and astringent contrasts in Lautrec's most expressive manner. Octave Maus is said to have acquired this picture in 1896, perhaps directly from the Manzi-Joyant exhibition at which the bordello scenes were shown by Lautrec in two small locked rooms.

C.M.

Gustave Moreau 1826-1898
b. Paris   *d.* Paris

33   *Salome,* 1876
     Oil on canvas 143.8 x 104.2 cm.

Collections: Louis Mante, Marseilles (sold Galerie Charpentier, Paris, Nov. 28, 1956 (no. 10));
Robert Lebel, Paris; Julius Weitzner, London; Huntington Hartford, New York.

Exhibitions: Paris, *Salon de 1876* (no. 1506); Paris, *Exposition Universelle Inernationale de 1878*
(no. 657); Paris, Galerie Georges Petit, *Gustave Moreau Exposition au profit des oeuvres du travail et des
pauvres bonteux,* 1906 (no. 76), lent by Louis Mante; Paris, Louvre, *Gustave Moreau,* June 1961 (no. 22),
lent by Huntington Hartford; New York, Museum of Modern Art, Dec. 4, 1961-Feb. 4, 1962, and
Art Institute of Chicago, Mar. 2-Apr. 15, 1962, *Odilon Redon — Gustave Moreau — Rudolphe Bresdin*
(no. 177), lent by Huntington Hartford; Los Angeles County Museum of Art, July 23-Sept. 1, 1974, and
San Francisco, California Palace of the Legion of Honor, Sept. 14-Nov. 3, 1974, *Gustave Moreau.*

Armand Hammer Collection Exhibitions: see pp. 17-18.
First exhibited Oklahoma City, 1971. Not exhibited Los Angeles, 1974; Moultrie.

Literature: *Salon de 1876, Palais de Champs Elysées, explication des ouvrages,* Paris, May 1, 1876,
p. 187, no. 1506; P. de Saint Victor, *La Liberté,* May 19, 1876; *Zigzags, Salon de 1876, Gustave Moreau,*
June 25, 1876, p. 2, no. 9; Charles Yriarte, "Le Salon de 1876," in *Gazette des beaux-arts,* vol. 13,
Paris, 1876, pp. 705-8, repr. p. 698 (sketch for *Salome*); Pierre de Savarus, *Le Salon de 1876, à vol
d'oiseau,* Paris, 1876, pp. 43-44; George Dufour, "Salon de 1876; le grand art et le petit art," *L'Artiste,*
July 1876, pp. 43-44; Victor de Swarte, *Lettres sur le Salon de 1876,* St.-Omer, 1876, p. 79; *Catalogue
officiel de l'Exposition Universelle Internationale de 1878 à Paris,* 1878, vol. 1, section 1 (Oeuvres d'Art),
p. 51, no. 657; Paul Mantz, "Paris Exposition Universelle, la peinture française," *Gazette des beaux-arts,*
vol. 1 (Dec. 1, 1878), p. 47; Charles L. Duval, *Les Beaux-Arts à l'Exposition de 1878,* impression et notes
d'artistes, Meaux, 1878, p. 127 (from *Le Publicateur,* Arrondissement de Meaux); *Exposition Universelle
de Paris, 1878, le livre d'or des exposants,* section 1 (Beaux-Arts), Paris, 1878, p. 10; Hippolyte Gautier
and Adrien Desprez, *Les Curiosités de l'Exposition de 1878,* Paris, 1878, p. 87; M. E. Bergerat, *Les
Chefs-d'oeuvre d'art à l'Exposition Universelle, 1878,* Paris, 1878, p. 156, plate 20 (photogravure Goupil
et Cie); Pierre de Savarus, *Dix Années d'art (souvenir des expositions),* Paris, 1879, pp. 89-91; J.C.L.
Dubosc de Pesquidoux, *L'Art au XIXe siècle, L'Art dans les deux mondes — peinture et sculpture,* Paris,
1881, vol. 1, p. 82, no. IV; J. K. Huysmans, *A Rebours,* Paris, 1884, pp. 71-76 (Engl. ed., trans. Robert
Baldick, *Against Nature,* Baltimore, 1959, pp. 63-67); Paul Leprieur, "Gustave Moreau," *L'Artiste,* Mar.
1889, pp. 175, 177, 180, May 1889, pp. 339, 350, 351, June 1889, pp. 444, 449, 450, 452; Jules-Antoine

Castagnary, *Salons, 1857-1879,* Paris, 1892, vol. 2, pp. 227-28; Gustave Larroumet, *Etudes de littérature et d'art,* Paris, 1896, pp. 227-78; Léon Thévenin, *L'Esthétique de Gustave Moreau,* Paris, 1897, pp. 9, 12-13; Gleeson White, "The Pictures of Gustave Moreau," *The Pageant,* 1897, p. 11; Léonce Bénédite, "Deux idéalistes, Gustave Moreau et E. Burne-Jones," *La Revue de l'art ancien et moderne,* Apr. 1899, pp. 265-90, repr.; Ary Renan, "Gustave Moreau," *Gazette des beaux-arts,* July 1899, pp. 62-63, repr. (heliogravure by J. Chauvet); Gustave Geffroy, *La Vie artistique,* ser. 6, chap. XVI, Paris, 1900, pp. 143-47; Henri Franz, "The New Gustave Moreau Gallery," *Magazine of Art,* vol. 24 (1900), pp. 99-104; Gustave Larroumet, Institut de France, Académie des Beaux-Arts, *Notice historique sur la vie et les oeuvres de M. Gustave Moreau,* Paris, 1901, pp. 21-22, 29-30, repr. p. 36; *Principales Oeuvres de maître dans les musées et collections particulières* (intro. Georges Desvallières), Musée National Gustave Moreau, Paris, 1906, no. 9 (heliogravure by J. Chauvet; Mante Coll.); Gustave Geffroy, *L'Oeuvre d'art, l'oeuvre de Gustave Moreau,* Paris, 1906, pp. 5, 9, 26-27; *Gustave Moreau Exposition au profit des oeuvres du travail et des pauvres honteux* (preface Robert de Montesquiou), catalogue, Galerie Georges Petit, Paris, 1906, no. 76, p. 38 (Mante Coll.); Arthur Symons, *Studies in Seven Arts,* London, 1910, pp. 73-77; Jean Laran and León Deshairs, *L'Art de nôtre temps, Gustave Moreau,* Paris, 1912, pp. 71-72, plate 28; *L'Oeuvre de Gustave Moreau* (intro. Georges Desvallières), Musée National Gustave Moreau, Paris, 1913, no. 9, repr.; Anon., *Gustave Moreau (Les Peintres illustrés, no. 55),* Paris, 1914, pp. 69-70; "Lettres de Georges Rouault a André Suarès," in *L'art et les artistes,* vol. 13, no. 66, Paris, 1926, p. 223, repr.; *Catalogue de la Vente Collection Louis Mante,* sale catalogue, Galerie Charpentier, Paris, 1956, no. 10, plate 111; Ragnar von Holten, *L'Art fantastique de Gustave Moreau,* Paris, 1960, pp. 19-20, repr. plate III in color; *Catalogue de l'Exposition Gustave Moreau,* Musée de Louvre, Paris, 1961, p. 22, no. 22, plate II (Huntington Hartford Coll.); Ragnar von Holten, "Le développement du personnage de Salomé à travers les dessins de Gustave Moreau," *L'Oeil,* Aug. 1961, pp. 44-51, 72; John Rewald, Dore Ashton, and Harold Joachim, *Odilon Redon — Gustave Moreau — Rudolphe Bresdin* (Museum of Modern Art, New York, in collaboration with the Art Institute of Chicago), New York, 1962, p. 116, no. 177; John Simon, "The Torments of Imagination," *Arts,* Feb. 1962, pp. 20-27, repr.; Daniel Grojnowski, "Les Mystères Gustave Moreau," *Revue générale des publications françaises et étrangères* (Editions de Minuit), vol. 19 (Mar. 1963), no. 190, pp. 225-38, sketch p. 237; *Catalogue of Paintings from the Huntington Hartford Collection in the Gallery of Modern Art,* New York, 1964, no. 14, repr. in color; Ragnar von Holten, *Gustave Moreau, Symbolist,* Stockholm, 1965, pp. 48-65, repr. p. 49; Max Gérard, *Dali,* New York, 1968, no. 169, detail repr. in color; *Important Impressionist and Modern Paintings and Drawings,* sale catalogue, Parke-Bernet Galleries, Inc., New York, Mar. 10, 1971, p. 52, no. 29, repr. in color; Mahonri Sharp Young, "The Hammer Collection: Paintings," *Apollo,* vol. 95 (June 1972), p. 452, repr. in color on cover; P. L. Mathieu, *Gustave Moreau: sa vie, son oeuvre; catalogue raisonné de l'oeuvre achevé,* Fribourg, 1976, pp. 121-24, repr. pp. 126, 127 (detail), 315 (cat. no. 157).

Salome represents the full flower of the tendency toward accumulation in Moreau's art as well as the apotheosis of one of the most notable and hermetic tendencies in late nineteenth century French art and literature. This tendency, which involved a slightly overripe enumerative presentation in both visual and verbal media, culminated in and was transformed by the work of Marcel Proust. More than one hundred related drawings are known for Moreau's *Salome* and its variant, *The Apparition,* of which the finished watercolor, now in the Louvre, was also exhibited in the Salon of 1876. The figure of Salome herself was studied in a wooden figure covered with wax and dressed, one of the dozen or so surviving pieces of sculpture by Moreau. Ragnar von Holten believes the subject to have been inspired by Flaubert's *Salammbô,* while Georges Duthuit traces it to Mallarmé's *Hérodiade,* but perhaps no specific source is needed for this theme of the *belle dame sans merci* (see Mario Praz, *The Romantic Agony*) so common to the *fin de siècle.*

The scene takes place under the surveillance of the Ephesian Artemis in a fantastic architecture of Moorish inspiration. J. K. Huysmans, who placed the painting in the possession of Des Esseintes, hero of *A Rebours,* described Salome as follows: "Her face composed, solemn, almost august, she begins the lascivious dance which must awaken the deadened senses of the aged Herod.... Concentrating, her eyes fixed like those of a sleepwalker, she sees neither the trembling Tetrarch nor her mother, the fierce Herodiade, who watches her, nor the hermaphrodite, or eunuch, who stands, sword in hand, at the foot of the throne." Moreau himself described Salome as "that woman nonchalantly strolling ... in the gardens recently stained by that horrible murder which terrified the executioner himself." Kaplan has called this picture, which has been known variously as *Salome,* the *Dance of Salome,* and *Salome Dancing before Herod,* Moreau's most "successful synthesis of precise delineation and free handling of oil pigment."

C.M.

Gustave Moreau 1826-1898

34   *King David*
Oil on canvas   230.0 x 137.6 cm.

Collections: Comtesse Roederer, Paris; Hector Brame, Paris; Walter P. Chrysler, Jr., New York.

Exhibitions: Paris, *Exposition Universelle Internationale de 1878* (no. 659); Toronto, the Art Gallery of Ontario, *The Sacred and Profane in Symbolist Art,* Nov. 1969 (no. 64); New York, Spencer A. Samuels & Co., Ltd., *Symbolists,* Nov. 1970 (no. 116); Los Angeles County Museum of Art, July 23-Sept. 1, 1974, and San Francisco, California Palace of the Legion of Honor, Sept. 14-Nov. 3, 1974, *Gustave Moreau.*

Armand Hammer Collection Exhibitions: see pp. 17-18.
First exhibited San Francisco, 1971. Not exhibited San Diego; Los Angeles, 1974; Los Angeles, 1975; Moultrie; West Palm Beach.

Literature: Catalogue *Officiel de l'Exposition Universelle Internationale de 1878 à Paris,* Paris, 1878, vol. 1, section 1 (Oeuvres d'Art), p. 51, no. 659; Pierre de Savarus, *Dix années d'art (souvenir des expositions),* Paris, 1879, pp. 94-95; J.C.L. Dubosc de Pesquidoux, *L'Art au XIXe siècle. L'Art dans les deux mondes — peinture et sculpture,* Paris, 1881, vol. 1, p. 84, no. VI; Claude Phillips, "Gustave Moreau," *Magazine of Art,* vol. 8, 1885, pp. 228-33, repr.; Paul Leprieur, "Gustave Moreau," *L'Artiste,* Mar. 1889, p. 175, May 1889, p. 357, June 1889, pp. 450-51; Jean Lorrain, *Sensations et Souvenirs,* Paris, 1895, p. 67; Ary Renan, "Gustave Moreau," *Gazette des beaux-arts,* Mar. 1899, pp. 192, 194, repr. (etching by M. Bracquemond); Henri Frantz, "The New Gustave Moreau Gallery," *Magazine of Art,* vol. 24 (1900), pp. 97-104, repr. p. 98 (engraving by Jonnard reprinted from Claude Phillips, "Gustave Moreau," *Magazine of Art,* 1885, pp. 228-33); Gustave Larroumet, Institut de France Académie des Beaux-Arts, *Notice historique sur la vie et les oeuvres de M. Gustave Moreau,* Paris, 1901, p. 36; *Catalogue sommaire des peintures, dessins, cartons et aquarelles du Musée Gustave Moreau,* Paris, 1902, pp. 9, 22, 23, 49-50, 55, 113; Louis Dimier, "L'Inspiration de Gustav Moreau," *Minerva,* Nov. 15, 1902, pp. 275-76; Camille Mauclair, "The Gustave Moreau Museum in Paris," *Art Journal* (London), 1905, p. 255, repr.; *Principales Oeuvres de maître dans les musées et collections particulières* (introd. Georges Desvallières), Musée National Gustave Moreau, Paris, 1906, no. 22 (heliogravure by J. Chauvet); Jean Laran and Léon Deshairs, *L'Art de Notre Temps, Gustave Moreau,* Paris, 1912, pp. 79-80, plate 33; Anon., *Gustave Moreau (Les Peintres illustrés,* no. 55), Paris, 1914, p. 74; Ragnar von Holten, *L'Art fantastique de Gustave Moreau,* Paris, 1960, plate 37; *Symbolists,* catalogue, Spencer A. Samuels & Co., Ltd., New York, 1970, p. 56, no. 116, repr.; J. Paladilhe and J. Pierre, *Gustave Moreau,* London, 1972, pp. 40, 122; P.-L. Mathieu, *Gustave Moreau: sa vie, son oeuvre; catalogue raisonné de l'oeuvre achevé,* Fribourg, 1976; pp. 132L — 132R, repr. p. 135 (detail), 318 (cat. no. 171).

Originally known simply as *David,* this picture has more recently borne the title *King David Meditating.* In it one sees that juxtaposition of disparate architectural and decorative elements so dear to Moreau. The cross-decorated temple lamp and the evangelist symbols on the capitals may refer to David as lineal ancestor of Christ. The painting comes close to being an allegory of the senses, with the aged psalmist surrounded by flowers, incense, and a burning lamp and clothed in jewels and rich materials. The subtle rhythms of the asymmetrical composition and the softening of the delicate and intricate detail in a poetic atmosphere distinguish Moreau's *King David* and other salon paintings from the works of empty formalism and banal sentiment by so many of his academic contemporaries. Of this kind of picture, Ary Renan wrote in the *Gazette des beaux-arts* in 1899, "His (Moreau's) idea was to equal, without deranging the harmony of line, and by the prestige alone of environing decorations, all the suggestions provoked in literature, music, and the theater."

C.M.

Note: As this catalogue went to press, the painting was being cleaned. Changes in color may occur when cleaning is completed which will differ from the color reproduced here. (Ed.)

Paul Gauguin 1848-1903
b. Paris   *d.* Fatu-Iwa, Marquesas Islands

35   *Bonjour M. Gauguin,* 1889
Oil on canvas, mounted on panel 74.9 x 54.6 cm.
Inscribed, lower left: *Bonjour M. Gauguin*

Collections: Mme Marie Henry, Le Pouldu, France; Galerie Barbazanges, Paris; Meyer Goodfriend, New York (sold American Art Galleries, New York, Jan. 4-5, 1923 (no. 107)); B. M. Alexander, New York; Howard Young Galleries, New York; Carlton Mitchell, Annapolis; Count Ivan Podgoursky, San Antonio; Mrs. Mary Ermolaev, Princeton, N.J. (sold Christie, Manson & Woods, Geneva, Switz., Nov. 6, 1969 (no. 169), repr. in cat.).

Exhibitions: Paris, Galerie Barbazanges, *Exposition D'Oeuvres Inconnues,* Oct. 10-30, 1919 (no. 2); New York, Wildenstein & Co., Inc., *A Retrospective Loan Exhibition for the Benefit of Les Amis de Paul Gauguin and the Penn Normal Industrial and Agricultural School,* Mar. 2-Apr. 18, 1936 (no. 14); Montreal, Museum of Fine Arts, *Manet to Matisse,* May-June 1949 (no. 14); Paris, Galerie Loize, *Les Amitiés du Peintre Georges-Daniel de Monfried et ses Reliques de Gauguin,* May 1951 (no. 108); Houston, Museum of Fine Arts, *Paul Gauguin, His Place in the Meeting of East and West,* Mar. 27-Apr. 25, 1954 (no. 15); Wichita Falls, Tex., The Museum Association of Midwestern Universities, Sept.-Oct. 1955 (no. 16); Tulsa, Philbrook Art Center, *Four Centuries of European Art,* Oct. 1956 (no. 34); Oklahoma City, Oklahoma Art Center, Nov. 1957 (no. 23), and Little Rock, Museum of Fine Arts, Dec. 1958 (no. 30), *Four Centuries of European Art;* Phoenix, Phoenix Art Museum, Feb. 1-26, 1961, and Oakland, Calif., Oakland Art Museum, Mar. 5-31, 1961, *One Hundred Years of French Painting,* 1860-1960 (no. 42), lent by Count Ivan Podgoursky; *Van Gogh, Gauguin and Their Circle,* catalogue, Christie, Manson & Woods (U.S.A.), Ltd., New York, Nov. 1968 (no. 9).

Armand Hammer Collection Exhibitions: see pp. 17-18.
First exhibited Memphis, 1969. Not exhibited Los Angeles, 1974.

Literature: Charles Chassé, *Gauguin et le groupe de Pont-Aven,* Paris, 1921, pp. 48-50; *American Art Journal,* vol. 20 (1923-24), p. 275; Jean de Rotonchamp, *Gauguin,* Paris, 1925, p. 70; *Canadian Art,* vol. 6 (Summer, 1949), p. 176, repr.; J. Loize, *Les Amitiés du peintre Georges-Daniel de Monfried et ses reliques de Gauguin,* catalogue, Galerie Loize, Paris, 1951, pp. 86-87, no. 108; Charles Chassé, *Gauguin et son temps,* Paris, 1955, pp. 70, 79; M. Malingue, "Du Nouveau sur Gauguin," *L'Oeil,* July-Aug. 1959, p. 38; John Rewald, *Le Post-Impressionisme,* Paris, 1961, p. 176; George Boudaille, *Gauguin,* London, 1964, pp. 89, 130, repr. in color; Georges Wildenstein, *Gauguin,* Paris, 1964, pp. 121-22, no. 321; *Art in America,* Sept. 1969, p. 15, repr.; *Art News,* Sept. 1969, p. 26, repr.; *Apollo,* Oct. 1969, p. IX, repr.; *Connaissance des arts,* Oct. 1969, p. 67, repr.; *Apollo,* Feb. 1970, p. 170, repr.; *Connoisseur,* Feb. 1970, p. 116, repr.; Frank Davis, "A Royal Record of Portraiture," *Country Life,* Feb. 5, 1970, pp. 302-3, repr.; Mahonri Sharp Young, "The Hammer Collection: Paintings," *Apollo,* vol. 95 (June 1972), p. 452.

In 1889 Gauguin and the painters working with him transferred their Breton activities from Pont-Aven to Le Pouldu. In October of that year, they moved to an inn kept by Marie Henry and soon thereafter began decorating its walls with paintings and sculpture. Gauguin's *Bonjour Monsieur Gauguin* occupied the upper panel of a door in the inn. There are two existing versions of the composition, and both Georges Wildenstein and Denys Sutton are agreed that the Hammer picture is the one originally fastened to the door at Le Pouldu, while the Prague version precedes it or is a later replica. This picture is distinguished from the Prague version by a somewhat more unified composition and more consistent brushwork.

C.M.

Bonjour Mr Gauguin

Sir John Everett Millais 1829-1896
b. Southampton, England   *d.* London

36   *Caller Herrin',* 1881
Oil on canvas 110.5 x 79.0 cm.
Signed with a monogram and dated, lower right

Collections: Fine Art Society, London, purchased from the artist, Feb. 15, 1882; Walter Dunlop, June 21, 1882 (sold Christie's, London, Mar. 12, 1904 (no. 78)); Thomas Agnew & Sons, Ltd., London, and sold to Stephen G. Holland (sold Christie's, London, June 25, 1908 (no. 77)); Thomas Agnew & Sons, Ltd., London, and sold to Sir Thomas Dewar (sold Christie's, London, Nov. 29, 1918 (no. 91)); bought by Gooden & Fox, London, and sold to Viscount Leverhulme (sold Anderson Galleries, New York, Feb. 17, 1926 (no. 179)); Alvan T. Fuller, Boston.

Exhibitions: London, Fine Art Society, 1882; Edinburgh, Royal Scottish Academy, 1883 (no. 322); Manchester, Corporation of Manchester Art Galleries, 1885; London, Grosvenor Gallery, 1886 (no. 52); Boston, Boston Art Club, *Fuller Collection,* 1928 (no. 14); Boston, Museum of Fine Arts, *A Memorial Exhibition of the Collection of the Honorable Alvan T. Fuller,* 1959 (no. 34).

Armand Hammer Collection Exhibitions: see pp. 17-18.
First exhibited Houston, 1979-80. Not exhibited Moultrie.

Literature: Sir Walter Armstrong, *Sir John E. Millais: His Life and Works,* London, 1885 (no. 2 in the series *The Art Annual*), p. 19; John Ruskin, *Notes on the Principal Pictures of Sir John Everett Millais Exhibited at the Grosvenor Gallery, 1886,* London, 1886, pp. 17-18; J. G. Millais, *The Life and Letters of Sir John Everett Millais,* London, 1899, vol. 2, pp. 128, 480; M. H. Speilmann, *Millais and His Works,* Edinburgh and London, 1898, pp. 38, 122, 146, 175, 179.

Few of Millais' paintings so brilliantly display as this picture does, his control of the brush and his superb ability as a pure painter. Yet, in viewing this ravishingly beautiful girl, chin in hand, gazing into the distance, pensive and melancholy, one forgets all technical virtuosity, just as one ignores the marvelous execution of the herrings, which so impressed John Ruskin. Beatrice Buckstone, the subject of the picture, was the daughter of a well-known actor and became one of Millais' favorite models. The painter envisages her as having just sung an old Scottish folk song:

> *Come buy my bonny caaler herrin'*
> *Six a penny caaler from the sea.*

"Caaler" means fresh, and this gives the painting its title.

Ruskin, who loved adolescent beauty, was enthralled by the painting. In a lecture he said, "As a piece of art, I should myself put (it) highest of all yet produced by the Pre-Raphaelite school." In a letter of June 2, 1882, to Mrs. Arthur Stevens he elaborated: "*Caller Herrin'* is a life-size sketch — or little more than a sketch — but with all the power of a finished picture, of a fisher girl about fourteen sitting with loose hair under a bank at the edge of the beach, with one hand on her basket (with two fish in it), her chin resting on the other, and her dark eyes lifted to the sky — the most pathetic single figure I ever saw in my life — though there is no sign of distress about the girl. She has good strong shoes and dress, nothing to indicate hard life but a little bloodstain on the hand from the fish; but quite unspeakably tragic, and such painting as there has not been since Tintoret."

J.W.

Emile Bernard 1868-1941
b. Lille, France   *d.* Paris

37   *Wheat Harvest,* 1889
Oil on canvas 72.4 x 91.1 cm.
Signed and dated, lower left: *E. Bernard 1889*

Collections: Clement Altarriba (son-in-law of the artist), Paris; Wildenstein & Co., Inc., New York; Mr. and Mrs. Richard Sussman, New York; Findlay Galleries, Inc., Chicago.

Armand Hammer Collection Exhibitions: see pp. 17-18.
First exhibited Memphis, 1969. Not exhibited Los Angeles, 1974; Los Angeles, 1975.

Literature: John Rewald, *Post Impressionism,* New York, 1956, repr. p. 285; *Connoisseur,* Nov. 1966, repr. p. XCIII; *Art Journal,* Winter, 1966-67, repr. p. 195; Mahonri Sharp Young, "Hammer Collection: Paintings," *Apollo,* vol. 95 (June 1972), p. 452.

The harvesting of wheat was among the favorite themes of the group gathered around Gauguin in Brittany during the years 1889-90. Bernard treated the subject in painting in 1888 and in a print in 1889, the year of this picture, and Gauguin also painted Breton haymakers in 1889 (see his *Breton Landscape* in the De Sylva Collection of the Los Angeles County Museum of Art). Bernard, forbidden by his father to join Gauguin at Pont-Aven, passed the summer of 1889 at Saint-Briac, where this picture was probably painted. One sees in the flat color areas reminiscences of the Japanese prints so popular with the Pont-Aven group, and in the outlining of the shapes the "cloisonnism" identified in their work by Edouard Dujardin. At this particular moment, Bernard had carried flatness and clear separation of colors considerably farther than Gauguin, although his facture (and Gauguin's of this period) recalls Cézanne's version of the Impressionist commalike brushwork with its groups of parallel strokes. In the cross on the distant hill, one can see perhaps a forecast of the mystical Catholicism that was increasingly to preoccupy Bernard.

C.M.

108

Vincent van Gogh 1853-1890
b. Zundert, Holland   *d.* Auvers-sur-Oise, France

38   *Garden of the Rectory at Nuenen,* 1885
Oil on canvas, mounted on panel 53.0 x 78.2 cm.

Collections: Oldenzeel Gallery, Rotterdam, 1903; Jan Smith Alblasserdam (sold Mak van Waaij, Amsterdam, Feb. 10, 1919 (no. 30), repr. in cat.; L.J. Smit, Kinderdijk; Leo C. Smit, Kinderdijk, 1952 (sold Parke-Bernet Galleries, Inc., New York, Nov. 20, 1968 (no. 37)); Spencer A. Samuels & Co., Ltd., New York; Fletcher Jones, Los Angeles.

Exhibitions: Rotterdam, Oldenzeel Gallery, *Van Gogh,* 1904 (no. 31); The Hague, Gemeentemuseum, *Vincent van Gogh,* Mar. 30-May 17, 1953 (no. 31); Otterloo, Rijksmuseum Kröller-Müller, *Vincent van Gogh,* May 24-July 19, 1953 (no. 18); Amsterdam, Stedelijk Museum, *Vincent van Gogh,* July 23-Sept. 20, 1953 (no. 18); Dordrecht Museum, *Boem, Bloem en Plant,* July 16-Aug. 31., 1955 (no. 52); Paris, Musée Jacquemart-André, *Vincent van Gogh,* Feb.-Mar. 1960 (no. 11).

Armand Hammer Collection Exhibitions: see pp. 17-18.
First exhibited Washington, D.C., 1970. Not exhibited Los Angeles, 1974; Los Angeles, 1975; Moultrie.

Literature: *The Letters of Vincent van Gogh to His Brother,* 1872-1886, London, Boston, and New York, 1927, vol. 2, Letter 394, pp. 456-58; J.B. de la Faille, *L'Oeuvre de Vincent van Gogh, catalogue raisonné,* Paris and Brussels, 1928, vol. 1, no. 67, vol. 2, plate XX (measurements incorrect); Dr. Walter Vanbeselaere, *De Hollandsche Periode (1880-1885) in Het Werk van Vincent van Gogh,* Antwerp, 1937, pp. 294, 352, 414; J.B. de la Faille, *Vincent van Gogh* (preface Charles Terrasse), Paris, 1939, p. 79, no. 73 (measurements incorrect); J.B. de la Faille, *The Works of Vincent van Gogh: His Paintings and Drawings,* Amsterdam, London, and New York, 1970, pp. 66, 614, no. F67, repr. p. 67; *Impressionist and Modern Paintings and Sculptures,* sale catalogue, Sotheby & Co., London, Apr. 15, 1970, p. 55, no. 26, repr. in color.

In the late winter of 1885-86, van Gogh wrote to his brother, "When there was snow, I...painted a few studies of our garden,"and J.B. de la Faille dates this picture to January, 1885. The scene is taken from the presbytery at Nuenen, the small town in which van Gogh's father was vicar and where Vincent lived with his family for two years before going to France. The distant tower occurs in several pictures of the time, and there exist another painting and two drawings directly related to this scene (J.B. de la Faille, nos. 185, 1133, 1234). The picture projects the bleakness

Vincent felt around him in the winter of 1885, a bleakness that permeates both his landscapes and his figure studies. It is among the last of his "Dutch" pictures, worked out in the dark tonalities of the Hague School, its drawing perhaps indebted to the English illustrations he knew so well. The extreme lightness of the sky forecasts the future lightening of van Gogh's palette and suggests that interest in color to which he referred constantly in his letters of the period.

C.M.

Vincent van Gogh 1853-1890

39   *Lilacs,* 1887
      Oil on canvas 27.3 x 35.3 cm.

Collection: Drs. Fritz and Peter Nathan, Zurich.

Armand Hammer Collection Exhibitions: see pp. 17-18.
First exhibited Oklahoma City, 1971. Not exhibited Los Angeles, 1975; Moultrie.

Literature: J.B. de la Faille, *The Works of Vincent van Gogh: His Paintings and Drawings,* Amsterdam, London, and New York, 1970, p. 142, no. 286b.

Van Gogh was preoccupied with bringing more intense color into his pictures long before his move to Paris in 1886. However, it was only under the direct impact of the paintings he saw in the French capital that he began to use color freely, applying it with an increasingly divisionist brushstroke. Toward the fall of 1887, Vincent wrote to the English painter Levens, "I have lacked money for paying models else I had entirely given myself to figure painting. But I have made a series of color studies in painting, simply flowers, red poppies, blue cornflowers and myosotis, white and red roses, yellow chrysanthemums — seeking oppositions of blue with orange, red and green, yellow and violet, seeking *les tons rompus et neutres* to harmonize brutal extremes. Trying to render intense color and not a gray harmony." The present picture is, no doubt, one of these studies.

C.M.

Vincent van Gogh 1853-1890

40   *The Sower,* ca. 1888
      Oil on canvas 33.6 x 40.4 cm.

Collections: Mme J. van Gogh-Bonger, Amsterdam; Montross Gallery, New York, 1921; the
Reverend Theodore Pitcairn, Bryn Athyn, Pa.

Exhibitions: New York, Montross Gallery, Oct. 1920; Philadelphia Museum of Art, Summer Loan, 1960,
lent by the Reverend Theodore Pitcairn.

Armand Hammer Collection Exhibitions: see pp. 17-18.
First exhibited Memphis, 1969. Not exhibited San Diego; Los Angeles, 1974; Los Angeles, 1975; Moultrie.

Literature: *Important Impressionist and Modern Drawings, Paintings and Sculpture,* sale catalogue,
Christie, Manson & Woods, London, May 2, 1969, p. 46, no. 58, repr. opp. p. 46; J.B. de la Faille, *The
Works of Vincent van Gogh: His Paintings and Drawings,* Amsterdam, London, and New York, 1970,
pp. 240, 634, no. 575a, repr.; P. Lecaldano, *Van Gogh,* Milan, 1971, vol. 2, p. 212, no. 566., repr.

The sower was a theme that fascinated van Gogh throughout his career, partly because of his Millet-inspired identification with the peasant subject and partly for his deep-seated associations with fertility and generation. This version of the subject is unique in showing the sower's figure placed against a silhouette of Arles, something van Gogh otherwise reserved for pictures of reapers or plowed fields (J.B. de la Faille, nos. 465, 545). The character of the brushwork and the nature and intensity of the color suggest a date in late 1888 or early 1889, conceivably even one as late in 1889 as van Gogh's stay in the hospital of Saint-Rémy. The size and intensity of the blue-purple field, "compulsive in its excess" (Meyer Schapiro), swallow the figure, adding to the picture's disharmonious scale relationships. This does not, however, detract from the power of this small canvas.

C.M.

Vincent van Gogh 1853-1890

41 *Hospital at Saint-Rémy,* 1889
Oil on canvas 90.2 x 71.1 cm.

Collections: A. Schuffenecker, Paris; Galerie E. Druet, Paris, 1907; Dr. J. Keller, Paris, 1908-10; Galerie E. Druet, Paris, 1910; Paul von Mendelssohn-Bartholdy, Berlin, 1911; Paul Rosenberg & Co., New York; Norton Simon, Los Angeles, 1964 (sold Parke-Bernet Galleries Inc., New York, May 5, 1971 (no. 48)).

Exhibitions: Paris, Galerie E. Druet, *Vincent van Gogh,* Jan. 6-18, 1908 (no. 16); Berlin, Galerie Paul Cassirer, *Vincent van Gogh,* May-June 1914 (no. 65); Amsterdam, Stedelijk Museum, *Vincent van Gogh en Zijn Tijdgenooten,* Sept. 6-Nov. 2, 1930 (no. 92); Frankfurt, Städelsches Kunstinstitut, *Ausstellung von Meisterwerken moderner Malerei, vom Abbild sum Sinnbild,* June 3-July 3, 1931 (no. 69).

Armand Hammer Collection Exhibitions: see pp. 17-18.
First exhibited Oklahoma City, 1971.

Literature: *Aesculape,* 13th year, no. 10 (Nov. 1923), p. 250, repr.; Louis Piérard, *La Vie tragique de Vincent van Gogh,* Paris, 1924, p. 184, repr.; Roch Grey, *Vincent van Gogh,* Rome, 1924 repr.; *Aesculape,* 16th year, no. 6 (June 1926), p. 158; Florent Fels, *Vincent van Gogh,* Paris, 1928, p. 171, repr.; J.B. de la Faille, *L'Oeuvre de Vincent van Gogh, catalogue raisonné,* Paris and Brussels, 1928, vol. 1, no. 643, vol. 2, plate CLXXIX; Victor Doiteau and Edgar Leroy, *La Folie de van Gogh* (preface Paul Gachet), Paris, 1928, p. 64, repr.; *The Further Letters of Vincent van Gogh to His Brother,* 1886-1889, London, Boston, and New York, 1929, vol. 3, Letter 610, p. 400; *Vincent van Gogh en Zijn Tijdgenooten,* catalogue, Stedelijk Museum, Amsterdam, 1930, p. 18, no. 92; *Ausstellung von Meisterwerken moderner Malerei, vom Abbild zum Sinnbild,* catalogue, Städelsches Kunstinstitut, Frankfurt, 1931, p. 26, no. 69; John Rewald, "Van Gogh en Provence," *L'Amour de l'art,* vol. 17 (Oct. 1936), p. 297, repr.; W. Scherjon and W. Jos. de Gruyter, *Vincent van Gogh's Great Period,* Amsterdam, 1937, p. 205, repr.; J.B. de la Faille, *Vincent van Gogh* (preface Charles Terrasse), Paris, 1939, p. 446, no. 648, repr.; Dr. François-Joachim Beer. *Du Démon de van Gogh* (after *Van Gogh à l'asile,* by Dr. Edgar Leroy), Nice, 1945, p. 75; J.B. de la Faille, *The Works of Vincent van Gogh: His Paintings and Drawings,* Amsterdam and New York, 1970, pp. 256, 636, no. F643, repr. p. 257; *Highly Important 19th and 20th Century Paintings, Drawings, & Sculpture from the Private Collection of Norton Simon,* sale catalogue, Parke-Bernet Galleries, Inc., New York, 1971, p. 92, no. 48, repr. in color; P. Lecaldano, *Van Gogh,* Milan, 1971, vol. 2. p. 223, no. 720, repr.; Mahonri Sharp Young, "The Hammer Collection: Paintings," *Apollo,* vol. 95 (June 1972), p. 452, repr. plate VI in color p. 448.

Van Gogh stayed at the hospital at Saint-Rémy for almost exactly one year, from May 1889 until May 1890, and took its gardens and surroundings as this the subject for many of his pictures. In the fall of 1889, he wrote to his brother Theo that he had "two views of the park and the asylum," one of which was undoubtedly this work. Only one other painting (J.B. de la Faille, no. 653) shows a substantial portion of the façade of the hospital. In the squared rendering of the building, one sees in this picture the remnants of an older style, while the flamelike brushwork of the trees, which Vincent saw as "warped as in old wood," announces the style for which he has become best known. Few of van Gogh's pictures show as well as this the tendency of his brushstrokes to cling to the surface of the canvas. During the last three years of his life, his paint application showed an increased density as well as intensity.

C.M.

Pierre Bonnard 1867-1947
b. Fontenay-aux-Roses, France   *d.* Cannet, France

42   *Street Scene,* ca. 1902
Oil on paper, mounted on board 53.3 x 69.8 cm.
Signed, lower right: *Bonnard*

Collections: Viscount Jowitt, London; Noel Coward, London; Sotheby & Co., London (sold
Apr. 18, 1956 (no. 144)); Schoneman Galleries, New York; Christie, Manson & Woods, London (sold
Dec. 1, 1967 (no. 37)).

Exhibitions: Scotland, Edinburgh Festival, *Bonnard and Vuillard,* Aug. 1948 (no. 55), repr. p. 7 in cat.;
London, Roland, Browse and Delbanco, *Bonnard,* 1950 (no. 16), repr. in cat.; London, Redfern Gallery,
French Paintings, Oct. 30-Nov. 22, 1952 (no. 53).

Armand Hammer Collection Exhibitions: see pp. 17-18.
First exhibited New York City, 1968. Not exhibited Los Angeles, 1975.

Literature: *Modern and French 19th Century Drawings, Paintings and Sculpture,* sale catalogue,
Sotheby & Co., London, 1956, no. 144, repr.; *L'Oeil,* Sept. 1956, p. 44; *Bonnard* (introd. Denys Sutton),
catalogue, Farber Gallery, London, 1957, p. 12, repr. plate 5 in color; Jean and Henry Dauberville,
Bonnard, catalogue raisonné de l'oeuvre peint, 1888-1905, Paris, vol. 1, 1965, p. 26, no. 269, repr.;
Important Impressionist and Modern Drawings, Paintings and Sculpture, sale catalogue, Christie,
Manson & Woods, London, 1967, p. 34, no. 37, repr. in color.

Although the relatively muted tones, small-scale
paint application, and areas of bare canvas in
this picture recall the early style Bonnard shared
with Vuillard, one begins to sense the richness of
Bonnard's later color in the red-blue contrasts.
Two strong verticals hold the composition firmly
in place, making it almost a triptych, a favorite
Nabi format.

C.M.

Pierre Bonnard 1867-1947

43   *Nude against the Light,* 1909
      Oil on canvas 123.8 x 54.6 cm.
      Signed, lower left: *Bonnard*

Collections: Galerie Bernheim-Jeune, acquired from Bonnard, Jan. 8, 1909; Henri Bernstein, Paris, purchased Jan. 8, 1910; repurchased by Galerie Bernheim-Jeune, Paris, June 9, 1911; Emile Maysisch, Paris; Marianne Feilchenfeldt, Zurich; Ragnar Moltzau, Oslo; Michael P. Couturier, Neuilly-sur-Seine; Adler Collection, London (sold Parke-Bernet Galleries, Inc., New York, Mar. 21, 1962 (no. 80)); Galerie der Spiegel, Cologne; Alex Léfèvre Gallery, London; Norton Simon, Los Angeles (sold Parke-Bernet Galleries, Inc., New York, May 5, 1971 (no. 59)).

Exhibitions: Zurich, Kunstahaus, *Bonnard,* 1949; Copenhagen, Ny Carlsberg Glyptotek, *Fra Renoir til Villon, Franske Malerier eg. Udlaant fra Ragnar Moltzau Samling,* June 21-Aug. 1, 1956 (hors cat.); The Hague, Gemeentemuseum, *Collection Moltzau,* Apr.-June 1957 (no. 15); Scotland, Edinburgh Festival, and London, Tate Gallery, *Bonnard,* 1958 (no. 13); Copenhagen, Ny Carlsberg Glyptotek, *Documenta III,* 1959; Paris, Galerie Europe, *Itinéraire sur Trois Génerations,* June-July 1960 (no. 4); London, Alex Léfèvre Gallery, *XIXth and XXth Century French Paintings,* Oct.14-Nov. 13, 1965 (no. 1).

Armand Hammer Collection Exhibitions: see pp. 17-18.
First exhibited Oklahoma City, 1971. Not exhibited Los Angeles, 1975; Moultrie.

Literature: Gustave Cuquiot, *Bonnard,* Paris, 1922, plate 5, *Art and Auctions,* vol. 6, no. 121 (Feb. 28, 1962), pp. 29, 35; *Important Modern Paintings, Drawings, Bronzes,* sale catalogue, Parke-Bernet Galleries, Inc., New York, 1962, no. 80, repr.; *Arts,* Mar. 1962, repr. p. 13; *Apollo,* Oct. 1965, repr. p. 338; Jean and Henry Dauberville, *Bonnard, catalogue raisonné de l'oeuvre peint, 1888-1905,* Paris, vol. 2, 1968, no. 528, repr. p. 140; *Highly Important 19th and 20th Century Paintings, Drawings & Sculpture from the Private Collection of Norton Simon,* sale catalogue, Parke-Bernet Galleries, Inc., New York, 1971, no. 59, p. 114, repr. in color.

Strongest as a colorist, weakest as a draftsman, Bonnard was often at his best when a canvas of firmly marked shape helped him structure his composition. In this picture the rectangular shapes at the top and left side assist in giving firmness, as do the value contrasts caused by the backlighting of the figure. For the rest, Bonnard is free to indulge the lavish richness of his purples, golds, and dark greens. Consistently attracted to the timeless theme of the bather, here he has used a languid pose recalling that of the traditional *La Source.* The picture was said by Gustave Cuquiot to date from 1908, although the Daubervilles assign it to 1909.

C.M.

Edouard Vuillard 1868-1940
b. Cuiseaux, France   *d.* La Baule, France

44 *In the Bus,* ca. 1895
    Oil on board 25.0 x 22.9 cm.
    Signed, lower right: *E. Vuillard*

Collections: Georges Seligmann, New York; Dalzell Hatfield Galleries, Los Angeles; Stephen Hahn Gallery, New York.

Armand Hammer Collection Exhibitions: see pp. 17-18.
First exhibited New York City, 1968. Not exhibited Memphis; Los Angeles, 1974; Los Angeles, 1975; Moultrie.

Literature: Mahonri Sharp Young, "The Hammer Collection: Paintings," *Apollo,* vol. 95 (June 1972), p. 452.

The *tachiste* paint application, which results in an all-over decorative pattern, and the predominance of low-keyed golden browns are characteristic of Vuillard at this date. The subject of the painting is by no means clear.

C.M.

Edouard Vuillard 1868-1940

45   *At the Seashore,* ca. 1904
      Oil on panel   21.6 x 21.6 cm.
      Signed, lower left: *E. Vuillard*

Collections: Joseph Hessel, Paris; Alfred Daber, Paris; Sam Salz, New York; Mr. and Mrs. Henry R. Luce, New York.

Exhibitions: Paris, Musée du Louvre, Pavillion Marsan, *Vuillard,* 1938; Paris, Galerie Charpentier, *Vuillard,* 1946; New York, Museum of Modern Art, and Cleveland Museum of Art, *Edouard Vuillard,* 1954, p. 103 in cat.; Toronto, Art Gallery of Ontario, Sept. 11-Oct. 24, 1971, San Francisco, California Palace of the Legion of Honor, Nov. 18, 1971-Jan. 2, 1972, and Chicago, Art Institute of Chicago, Jan. 29-Mar. 12, 1972, *Edouard Vuillard,* no. 59.

Armand Hammer Collection Exhibitions: see pp. 17-18.
First exhibited Memphis, 1969. Not exhibited Los Angeles, 1971-72; Los Angeles, 1975; Moultrie.

Literature: Jacques Salomon, *Vuillard,* Paris, 1968, no. 100, as *Lucie Hessel devant la Mer,* repr. in color; François Daulte, "Hammer en dix chefs-d'oeuvre," *Connaissance des arts,* Sept. 1970, p. 85, repr. in color; John Russell, *Edouard Vuillard,* 1868-1940, catalogue, Art Gallery of Ontario, Toronto, 1971, p. 231, plate 59; Mahonri Sharp Young, "The Hammer Collection: Paintings," *Apollo,* vol. 95 (June 1972), p. 452, repr. plate VIII in color, p. 450.

"This little painting," wrote Jacques Salomon, "is like a cry from the heart, the echo of which ravished me when I admired it on Lucie Hessel's mantelpiece; the touch is so alive, so alert, so completely submissive to the rhythm of Vuillard's feeling." Vuillard first met Mme Hessel in 1900, and it was in her apartment in the Rue de Rivoli that he henceforth found most of his sitters, the most constant of these being Mme Hessel herself.

She was, in Jacques Salomon's words, "beautiful and elegant, without being pretty. Mme Hessel joined great qualities of judgment and feeling to a real distinction. Vuillard devoted to her a constant friendship, which for forty years was not troubled by the slightest cloud." Lucie Hessel was the wife of Joseph Hessel, first director of the Galerie Bernheim-Jeune and later an important independent dealer in Rue La Boëtie.

C.M.

124

Edouard Vuillard 1868-1940

46   *Rue Lepic, Paris,* 1908
Tempera 165.1 x 47.0 cm.
Signed, lower right: *E. Vuillard*

Collections: Sam Salz, New York; Mr. and Mrs. Henry R. Luce, New York.

Exhibitions: Toronto, Art Gallery of Ontario, Sept. 11-Oct. 24, 1971; San Francisco, California Palace of the Legion of Honor, Nov. 18, 1971-Jan. 2, 1972, and Chicago, Art Institute of Chicago, Jan. 29-Mar. 12, 1972, *Edouard Vuillard,* no. 69.

Armand Hammer Collection Exhibitions: see pp. 17-18.
First exhibited Memphis, 1969. Not exhibited Los Angeles, 1975; Fukuoka; Nagoya; Nashville; Mexico City; Paris; Moultrie.

Literature: Claude Roger-Marx, *Vuillard et son temps,* Paris, 1945, p. 140 (original project, with additional twelve inches of sky, repr. p. 161); John Russell, *Edouard Vuillard, 1868-1940,* catalogue, Art Gallery of Ontario, Toronto, 1971, p. 232, plate 69; Mahonri Sharp Young, "The Hammer Collection: Paintings," *Apollo,* vol. 95 (June 1972), p. 452.

The tall, narrow format imposed by projects for decorative screens or room panels seems to have been particularly congenial to the Nabis. In this one, the matte paint application, leaving space for the support to show through, may possibly reflect Toulouse-Lautrec's influence on Vuillard. The composition, cut down by about a foot from its original dimensions, was one of a series of sketches of streets and squares of Paris for a projected room decoration for Henri Bernstein. Claude Roger-Marx reproduces it in its original state next to a similar panel of a park in Paris. The Rue Lepic runs into the Place Blanche in Montmartre, the center of Nabi activity.

C.M.

Edouard Vuillard 1868-1940

47   *Interior,* ca. 1910
      Oil on board 53.3 x 40.3 cm.
      Stamped, lower right: *E. Vuillard*

Collections: The Hanover Gallery, London; Edward Le Bas, Brighton (sold Christie, Manson & Woods, Geneva, Switzerland, Nov. 6, 1969 (no. 164)).

Exhibitions: London, Royal Academy of Arts, *From a Painter's Collection* (Edward Le Bas Coll.), Mar. 19-Apr. 28, 1963 (no. 120).

Armand Hammer Collection Exhibitions: see pp. 17-18.
First exhibited Washington, D.C., 1970. Not exhibited Los Angeles, 1975.

Literature: *Impressionist and Modern Drawings, Paintings and Sculpture,* sale catalogue, Christie, Manson & Woods, Geneva, Switzerland, 1969, no. 164, repr.

Lighter in tone than is common for Vuillard, this airy composition is held together by the rectangular forms of the window, doorway, and chair and by the strong vertical of the open door. The scene may be that of his studio on the Boulevard Malsherbes.

The stamped signature in the lower righthand corner of the picture is identified in Frits Lugt, *Les Marques de collections, de dessins & d'estampes* (Le Haye, 1956, Supplement, pp. 363-64, no. 2497a). After Vuillard's death, his sister and brother-in-law, M. and Mme K.-X. Roussel, put stamps (E. Vuillard or EV) on the works that remained in his studio as well as on a few that belonged to the family or to Vuillard's close friends.

J.W.

André Derain 1880-1954
b. Chatou, France   *d.* Garches, France

48   *Still Life with Basket, Jug and Fruit,* 1911
Oil on canvas   50.5 x 60.1 cm.
Signed, lower right: *a derain*

Collections: Galerie Simon, Paris; Galerie Matthieson, Berlin; Edward Le Bas, Brighton (sold Christie, Manson & Woods, Geneva, Switzerland, Nov. 6, 1969 (no. 165)).

Exhibitions: London, Arts Council of Great Britain, *20th Century French Paintings and Drawings,* 1943 (no. 10); London, Royal Academy of Arts, *From a Painter's Collection* (Edward Le Bas Coll.), Mar. 9-Apr. 28, 1963 (no. 161).

Armand Hammer Collection Exhibitions: see pp. 17-18.
First exhibited Washington, D.C., 1970. Not exhibited Los Angeles, 1974; Los Angeles, 1975; Moultrie.

Literature: *L'Esprit nouveau,* May 1921, repr.; *Impressionist and Modern Drawings, Paintings and Sculpture,* sale catalogue, Christie, Manson & Woods, Geneva, Switzerland, 1969, no. 165 repr.; Mahonri Sharp Young, "The Hammer Collection: Paintings," *Apollo,* vol. 95 (June 1972), p. 452.

At the same time that he was painting more clearly Cubist-derived works, Derain was also working in the flatter, heavier style of this picture. One sees the influence of Cubism in the stylization of the shapes, the paint application of the background, and the restricted palette. The particular range of dark hues employed in this picture was favored by Derain throughout his career, and the style of this work is in every way more prophetic of his future than were many of the paintings he executed at this time.

C.M.

Amedeo Modigliani 1884-1920
b. Livorno, Italy   *d.* Paris

49   *Woman of the People,* 1918
Oil on canvas 99.7 x 65.1 cm.
Signed, upper right: *Modigliani*

Collections: André Léfèvre, Paris; Blair Laing, Toronto; Dr. Armand Hammer, Los Angeles; Los Angeles County Museum of Art, gift of Dr. and Mrs. Armand Hammer, 1968.

Exhibitions: Brussels, Palais des Beaux-Arts, *Modigliani,* 1933 (no. 53); Paris, Petit Palais, *Les Maîtres de l'Art Indépendants, 1895-1937,* June-Oct. 1937 (no. 77); Paris, Musée National d'Art Moderne, *L'Oeuvre du XXe Siècle,* May-June 1952 (no. 73); London, Arts Council, *XXth Century Masterpieces,* 1952 (no. 67); Paris, Musée National d'Art Moderne, *Collection André Léfèvre,* Mar.-Apr. 1964 (no. 209).

Armand Hammer Collection Exhibitions: see pp. 17-18.
First exhibited New York City, 1968. Not exhibited Columbus; Little Rock; Oklahoma City; Los Angeles, 1975; Moultrie.

Literature: Maurice Raynal, *Peintres du XXe siècle,* Geneva, Switzerland, 1947, repr. plate 38 in color; Claude Roy, *Modigliani* (The Taste of Our Time), Geneva, Switzerland, 1958, p. 80, repr.; Maurice Raynal, *La Peinture française contemporaine,* Geneva, Switzerland, c. 1960, repr. plate 37 and on cover in color; *Modigliani* (Skira Color Prints), New York, n.d., plate 1; *Vente Léfèvre,* sale catalogue, Palais Galliéra, Paris, Nov. 25, 1965, repr.; Mahonri Sharp Young, "The Hammer Collection: Paintings," *Apollo,* vol. 95 (June 1972), p. 452.

This portrait of Germaine Lable, daughter of the concierge of the artist's close friend, the poet Max Jacob, was painted in 1918, two years before Modigliani's premature death at the age of thirty-six. The painting exemplifies Modigliani's distinctive ability to capture the unique character of his sitter through, or one might almost say despite, his personal, elegantly mannered style of portraiture. The elongated oval face, drooping shoulder lines and pursed lips were all favorite devices of the artist. The delicately balanced facial features and the graceful curves of hairline, scarf, and drapery reveal the artist's masterful draftsmanship. This commonplace woman of the people, seated in a basically static frontal position, is juxtaposed to the diagonal angle of the bed so that the curvilinear pattern of the head rail and pillow complements the curves in the figure and creates a dynamic interplay of compositional forces. The combination of spatial flatness and subtle distortion of linear and shape relationships results in a unified, highly evocative composition; the abstract rhythm of formal elements across the pictorial surface alone carries the weight of the personal content. It is precisely this way of conveying incisive characterization with the most elegant and sparse formal means that makes Modigliani so moving and original an artist.

C.M.

Chaim Soutine 1894-1943
b. Minsk, Lithuania *d.* Paris

50   *The Valet,* 1929
Oil on canvas 109.0 x 63.5 cm.
Signed, upper right: *Soutine*

Collections: Pierre Loeb; Marcel Fleischmann, Zurich; Leigh B. Block, Chicago; Paul Rosenberg, New York; Walter P. Chrysler, Jr., New York.

Exhibitions: New York, Museum of Modern Art, 1939-42; Cleveland Museum of Art, *Soutine,* Apr.-June 1952 (no. 462); Dayton Art Institute, Dayton, Ohio, *French Painting 1789-1929 from The Collection of Walter P. Chrysler, Jr.,* 1960; Provincetown, Mass., Chrysler Museum, *Controversial Century,* June 15-Sept. 3, 1962; Ottawa, National Gallery of Canada, *Soutine,* Sept. 27-Nov. 4, 1962.

Armand Hammer Collection Exhibitions: see pp. 17-18.
First exhibited Buffalo, 1978. Not exhibited Moultrie.

Literature: M. Sachs, "Soutine," *Creative Art,* Dec. 1932, pp. 273-78, repr.; M. Wheeler, *Soutine,* New York, 1950, p. 80, repr.

Soutine, the son of a poor tailor from Smilovitch, near Minsk, arrived in Paris in 1911, having studied painting in Wilno. Like his compatriot Chagall, he brought to the cosmopolitan School of Paris a new strain made up of the intense emotional life of a Jewish village and the visionary poetry that grew out of its frustrations and poverty. His tragic sense, which caused him to try to hang himself, is expressed in the distorted and tortured faces of his sitters — valets, bellboys, cooks — whom he portrayed with a mastery of brushwork and pigmentation unsurpassed among modern artists.

In the Hammer picture, painted at the end of the 1920s, this melancholy youth, seated astride a chair, seems ready to spring automatically to attention in spite of his trancelike state. The portrait reveals Soutine's terrible nervous energy, which he has poured into the twisted, elongated face. The pigment is squeezed onto the canvas and brushed with demonic frenzy. After completing a picture like this, Soutine is said to have been physically exhausted.

The Valet has hung on the walls of many museums, where, to the sensitive observer, it has always seemed like a bomb that might explode at any moment. Soutine's pictures are not easy to look at with tranquility.

J.W.

Georges Rouault 1871-1958
b. Paris   *d.* Paris

51   *Circus Girl,* 1939
Oil on paper 65.4 x 52.5 cm.
Signed, lower right: *G. Rouault*

Collections: Ambroise Vollard, Paris, until 1939; Edwin C. Vogel, New York; Perls Gallery, New York; Vladimir Golschmann, St. Louis; Stephen Hahn Gallery, New York.

Exhibitions: New York, Galerie Chalette, 1958; Tokyo, National Museum of Western Art, Oct. 1-Nov. 10, 1963; Kyoto, National Art Gallery of Kyoto, Nov. 20-Dec. 10, 1963.

Armand Hammer Collection Exhibitions: see pp. 17-18.
First exhibited New York City, 1968. Not exhibited Memphis; Los Angeles, 1974; Los Angeles, 1975; Moultrie.

Characters from the Bible and from the circus appear frequently in Rouault's paintings and drawings, the circus figures as early as 1915 and as late as 1956. *Circus Girl* was probably painted between 1938 and 1943, when the artist illustrated a book and published a portfolio of paintings with this subject. The first, *Le Cirque de l'étoile filante* (1938), contained seventeen etchings and eighty-two wood engravings. With its companion, *Passion* (1939), also illustrated by Rouault but composed by his friend, the poet André Suarès, these editions represented the two dominant themes of Rouault's oeuvre: the church and the cabaret, the sacred and the profane (see Pierre Courthion, *Georges Rouault,* London, 1962, pp. 254-55). In 1943 Rouault again depicted the circus in a series of paintings, which, together with his verse, were published as a portfolio called *Divertissements.* In a line from one of his poems, Rouault describes a harlequin as a wasp "golden yellow, and ivory black," a description that equally well applies to the *Circus Girl.* There are several representations by the artist of entertainers similar to the Hammer picture, at least four of which are head-and-shoulder portraits in profile (Courthion, nos. 374, 503, 505, 512). The latter range in date from 1933 to 1948.

The influence of Gustave Moreau, Rouault's teacher, is apparent in the rich pigmentation and dense texture of this painting. However, the use of heavy impasto and thick black line to define the colors is typically Rouault's.

M.E.

Maurice de Vlaminck 1876-1958
b. Paris   *d.* Paris

52   *Summer Bouquet*
Oil on canvas 65.4 x 54.7 cm.
Signed, lower left: *Vlaminck*

Collections: James Vigeveno Galleries, Los Angeles; Mr. and Mrs. Henry R. Luce, New York.

Armand Hammer Collection Exhibitions: see pp. 17-18.
First exhibited Kansas City, 1970. Not exhibited Los Angeles, 1974; Los Angeles, 1975; Moultrie.

Literature: Mahonri Sharp Young, "The Hammer Collection: Paintings," *Apollo,* vol. 95 (June 1972), p. 452.

Vlaminck was so prolific as a landscape painter that his vases of flowers are comparatively rare. Yet he did paint flower still lifes sporadically through most of his career. His handling of the thick, juicy paint, which is one of his most attractive talents, is beautifully displayed in this rather late work, especially in the petals of the flowers. De Stäel never produced a more brilliant display of palette-knife virtuosity.

J.W.

Marie Laurencin 1885-1956
b. Paris   *d.* Paris

53   *Women in the Forest,* 1920
Oil on canvas 81.0 x 100.7 cm.
Signed and dated, lower right: *Marie Laurencin 1920*

Collections: Paul Rosenberg, Paris; John Quinn, New York; Forrestal, New York; Martin Horrell,
New York; Leo Aarons, New York; Stephen Hahn Gallery, New York.

Exhibitions: New York, Art Center, *Memorial Exhibition of the John Quinn Collection,* Jan. 8-30, 1926;
Washington, D.C., Hirshhorn Museum and Sculpture Garden, *The Noble Buyer: John Quinn, Patron
of the Avant-Garde,* June 15-Sept. 4, 1978.

Armand Hammer Collection Exhibitions: see pp. 17-18.
First exhibited Memphis, 1969. Not exhibited Los Angeles, 1974; Los Angeles, 1975; Edinburgh; Moultrie.

Literature: Roger Allard, *Marie Laurencin (Les Peintres Français Nouveaux,* no. 9), Paris, 1921, repr.
p. 49; Forbes Watson, *John Quinn 1870-1925, Collection of Paintings, Water Colors, Drawings & Sculpture,*
Huntington, New York., 1926, p. 11, repr. p. 66; B. L. Reid, *The Man from New York,* New York, 1968,
pp. 470-71; Mahonri Sharp Young, "The Hammer Collection: Paintings," *Apollo,* vol. 95 (June 1972), p. 452.

Marie Laurencin was closely associated with the
Cubists before World War I and with the artists
who formed Cubist splinter movements after the
war, but her style was little affected by any of
them. Guillaume Apollinaire characterized her
painting in *The Cubist Painters* (trans. Lionel
Abel, New York, 1944): "Like the dance, it is
an infinitely gracious and rhythmical art of
enumeration." Her iconography of sylphlike girls
and gentle animals in an Arcadian landscape is
a personal lyric invention — suggestive rather
than literal. This large work, *Women in the
Forest,* seems to be a monumental restatement of
elements Laurencin had used in numerous small
paintings between 1917 and 1920.

J.W.

Marc Chagall
b. Vitebsk, Russia 1887

54   *Blue Angel*
Gouache and pastel 50.8 x 66.1 cm.

Collections: Frank Crowninshield, New York; Mr. and Mrs. Henry R. Luce, New York.

Exhibitions: New York, Galerie Chalette, 1958; Tokyo, National Museum of Western Art, Oct. 1-Nov. 10, 1963; National Art Gallery of Kyoto, Nov. 20-Dec. 10, 1963.

Armand Hammer Collection Exhibitions: see pp. 17-18.
First exhibited Memphis, 1969. Not exhibited San Diego; Los Angeles, 1974; Los Angeles, 1975; Moultrie.

Literature: Franz Meyer, *Marc Chagall, Life and Work,* New York, 1964, no. 672, repr. p. 757.

The theatrical blue-red color harmony of this work and its juxtaposition of normally unrelated figures, floating and dreamlike, are typical of Chagall. Although the angel may have been in Chagall's mind particularly because of the illustrations for the Bible he had been commissioned by Ambroise Vollard to do in the early 1920s, both it and the bouquet of flowers are common in his scenes of lovers and newlyweds. Franz Meyer suggests that the "new natural sensuousness" of the pictures of 1937-39 was the result of the increased security in Chagall's personal affairs during that time.

J.W.

Gilbert Stuart 1755-1828
b. North Kingston, Rhode Island   *d.* Boston

55   *Portrait of George Washington,* 1822
Oil on canvas 112.0 x 87.6 cm.

Collections: William D. Lewis, Philadelphia; Estate of William D. Lewis (on loan to Pennsylvania Academy of the Fine Arts, Philadelphia, 1881-1928); Howard Young Galleries, New York; Mr. and Mrs. Alfred G. Wilson, Detroit (sold Parke-Bernet Galleries, Inc., New York, December 10, 1970 (no. 12)).

Exhibitions: Detroit Institute of Arts, *The Eleventh Loan Exhibition American Colonial and Early Federal Art,* Feb. 4-Mar. 2, 1930 (no. 81), lent by Mr. and Mrs. Alfred G. Wilson; Detroit Institute of Arts, *Masterpieces of Painting from Detroit Private Collections,* Apr. 23-May 22, 1949 (no. 30), lent by Mr. and Mrs. Alfred G. Wilson; Los Angeles County Museum of Art, Aug. 6-Dec. 9, 1974; *Two Hundred Years of American Painting,* traveling exhibition, Bonn, Rheinisches Landesmuseum, Belgrade, Museum of Modern Art, Rome, Galleria D'Arte Moderna e Contemporanea, Warsaw, National Museum of Poland, June 1, 1976-Jan. 15, 1977.

Armand Hammer Collection Exhibitions: see pp. 17-18.
First exhibited Little Rock, 1970-71. Not exhibited Los Angeles, 1974; Los Angeles, 1975; Nashville; Moultrie.

Literature: Henry T. Tuckerman, *Book of the Artists,* New York, 1867, p. 120; George C. Mason, *Life and Works of Gilbert Stuart,* New York, 1879, p. 113; Elizabeth Bryant Johnston, *Original Portraits of Washington,* Boston, 1882, pp. 81-82; Mantle Fielding, *Gilbert Stuart's Portraits of Washington,* Philadelphia, 1923, p. 148, no. 30; Lawrence Park, *Gilbert Stuart: An Illustrated Descriptive List of His Works,* New York, 1926, vol. 2, p. 862, no. 31; John Hill Morgan and Mantle Fielding, *The Life Portraits of Washington and Their Replicas,* Philadelphia, 1931, p. 271, no. 31; G. A. Eisen, *Portraits of Washington,* New York, 1932, p. 126, repr. p. 255; *Important American Paintings, Sculpture and Drawings,* sale catalogue, Parke-Bernet Galleries, Inc., New York, 1970, p. 14, no. 12, repr. in color; Mahonri Sharp Young, "The Hammer Collection: Paintings," *Apollo,* vol. 95 (June 1972), p. 452.

Whatever Stuart's reasons were for leaving Ireland in 1793, he returned to America expecting to capitalize on the demand for portraits of George Washington. It was an astute and logical move for one of the greatest portrait painters of the period. Such was the stature of Washington, already the personification of the nation, that Stuart and his competitors, the Peales, found it profitable to devote a great part of their energy and time to recording his image.

Sittings in 1795 resulted in the Vaughan type of bust portrait, and in 1796 the President sat for the famous Athenaeum portrait, now shared between the Museum of Fine Arts, Boston and the National Portrait Gallery, Smithsonian Institution, Washington, D.C. When Senator William Bingham asked for a full-length portrait in 1796, the Athenaeum portrait was used as the model for the head in the composition, which became known as the Lansdowne type. The present half-length, painted for William D. Lewis in 1822, is based on the Lansdowne full-length, specifically on the later version now in the New York Public Library (Lenox Coll.), painted at the request of Peter Jay Munro. The basic composition is that of the Constable-Hamilton half-length of 1797, also in the New York Public Library.

L.C.

William Michael Harnett 1848 or 1851-1892
b. Clonakilty, Ireland   *d.* New York

56   *Still Life,* 1885
Oil on panel 34.9 x 26.2 cm.
Signed and dated, lower left: *WM Harnett 1885*

Collections: George Richmond, London (sold Richmond studio sale, Christie, Manson & Woods, London, May 1, 1897 (no. 4)); Lord Justice William Rann Kennedy (sold Christie, Manson & Woods, London, Feb. 19, 1971 (no. 177)).

Exhibitions: London, Royal Academy of Arts, May 1885 (no. 860); St. Helens, Victoria Park, London, *First Summer Exhibition,* 1892 (no. 105); Los Angeles County Museum of Art, Aug. 6-Dec. 9, 1974.

Armand Hammer Collection Exhibitions: see pp. 17-18.
First exhibited Oklahoma City, 1971. Not exhibited Los Angeles, 1974; Moultrie.

Literature: Algernon Graves, *The Royal Academy of Arts, A Complete Dictionary of Contributors and Their Work from Its Foundation in 1769 to 1904,* London, 1905, p. 395, no. 860; *Magazine of Art,* Feb. 1951, p. 66; Alfred Frankenstein, *After the Hunt: William Harnett and Other American Still Life Painters, 1870-1900,* Berkeley and Los Angeles, 1953 (2nd ed., 1969), p. 70-71; *Pictures, Drawings, Bronzes and Prints of American, Australian, Canadian, New Zealand and South African Interest,* sale catalogue, Christie, Manson & Woods, London, 1971, p. 49, no. 177, repr. in color; Mahonri Sharp Young, "The Hammer Collection: Paintings," *Apollo,* vol. 95 (June 1972), pp. 452, 454, repr. plate X in color p. 453.

Though Harnett's *trompe-l'oeil* painting has a counterpart in the history of European art, it stands as a culmination of the long tradition of American realism. Harnett's five years abroad had an effect on his work but did not erase the unique, personal elements of his style nor the stamp of forthright vision that characterizes so much of American painting.

Painted in Paris in 1885, this *Still Life* was sent to the Royal Academy in London, where it was noted in the *Times* as "one of the most miraculous representations. . .that we have ever seen." The writer undoubtedly was referring to the degree of realism of the painting. For, while the arrangement of solid objects in Harnett's *Still Life* does not permit the kind of visual deception typical of the more two-dimensional rack paintings in which flat objects such as cards and envelopes are mounted on a board, it nevertheless achieves an almost tangible extension into space. But Harnett achieves more than an illusion of three-dimensionality. In this

work, Harnett displays his particular genius in the highly sophisticated balance of color, form, and texture. Even the subtle shifts in hue among the various faded sheets of music are exploited to the fullest; and the qualities of paper, metal, leather, velvet, and wood are explored and juxtaposed so as to reveal the full visual scale.

Another almost identical painting at Yale University has been mistaken for this one, which was bought by George Richmond from the Royal Academy in 1885. The only obvious difference between the two, probably introduced to avoid exactly the kind of problem that has arisen, is the reversal of the printed word fragments on the roll of music protruding at the left and again on the top sheet of music at the front edge of the cabinet. Apparently, Harnett himself was a victim of this confusion, for on the back of Alfred Frankenstein's photograph of the Yale painting, an inscription in the artist's own hand identifies it as the George Richmond still life.

L.C.

John Singer Sargent 1856-1925
b. Florence, American parents   *d.* London

57   *Dr. Pozzi at Home,* 1881
Oil on canvas 204.5 x 111.5 cm.
Signed and dated, upper right: *John S. Sargent, 1881*

Collection: Estate of the Hon. Jean Pozzi (sold Palais Galliéra, Paris, Dec. 4, 1970 (no. 84)).

Exhibition: Los Angeles County Museum of Art, Aug. 6-Dec. 9, 1974.

Armand Hammer Collection Exhibitions: see pp. 17-18.
First exhibited San Francisco, 1971. Not exhibited Los Angeles, 1974; Moultrie.

Literature: *L'Art et les artistes,* vol. 4 (1905-7), p. 368, repr.; William Howe Downes, *John S. Sargent, His Life and Work,* Boston, 1925, pp. 10-11, 113; Hon. Evan Charteris, *John Sargent,* New York, 1927, p. 258; Charles Merrill Mount, *John Singer Sargent,* London, 1957, pp. 61, 65, 67, 69, 116, 153; Richard Ormond, *John Singer Sargent, Paintings, Drawings, Watercolors,* New York, 1970, p. 34; *Tableaux modernes, sculptures,* sale catalogue, Palais Galliéra, Paris, 1970, no. 84, repr., also in color on cover; Mahonri Sharp Young, "The Hammer Collection: Paintings," *Apollo,* vol. 95 (June 1972), repr. plate XI in color p. 455.

While there was still a decidedly youthful quality in Sargent's work in 1881, he was rapidly maturing as an artist. He had already been honored in the Salon of 1879 for the dramatic portrait of his teacher Carolus-Duran. In 1881 he received a medal second class, making him *"hors concours and a great swell,"* as he jokingly put it. Thus, the portrait *Dr. Pozzi at Home* was eagerly undertaken by an artist brimming with enthusiasm and confidence.

Innovative from the beginning, Sargent was never content with a formal, straightforward likeness. Even in the early portrait of Carolus, the teacher assumes a special vitality in a dynamic pose conveying force and movement. It was perhaps the influence of Impressionism that led Sargent to ask Mme Pailleron to pose out-of-doors for the full-length standing portrait of her that appeared in the Salon of 1880. Some of his great portraits are the most informal ones, catching the subject engaged in life. The portrait of Dr. Pozzi is a powerful statement of this kind. Moving beyond the snapshot effect that could so easily result from this approach, the artist brings to the painting much more than the experience of Carolus' studio. Certainly, his solid grasp of form and light, as shown in his rendering of his subject's head, reflects the method of his teacher. But Sargent's own personal gift, expanded and refined by a close study of the old masters, is affirmed. The drama of the painting is an extension of the artist's responses to the work of Velazquez and of Hals, which he had studied so closely in previous months. In gesture and movement, the figure is purely Baroque; and, despite the overt drama of the technically superb glazes, there is a subtlety of light and tone that could have had its source in Velazquez.

L.C.

148

John Singer Sargent 1856-1925

58   *Portrait of Mrs. Edward L. Davis and Her Son, Livingston Davis,* 1890
Oil on canvas 218.4 x 121.9 cm.
Signed, lower right: *John S. Sargent*

Collections: Edward Livingston Davis, Worchester, Mass.; Livingston Davis, Boston, Mass.;
Mrs. A. Winsor Weld, Boston, Mass. (sold Parke-Bernet Galleries, Inc., New York, Mar. 19-20, 1969
(no. 74)); James Graham & Sons, New York; Dr. and Mrs. Armand Hammer; Los Angeles County
Museum of Art (Frances and Armand Hammer Purchase Fund, 1969).

Exhibitions: New York, National Academy of Design, 1890; New York, Society of American Artists,
1891; Boston, Mass., Boston Art Museum, 1891; Chicago, *World's Columbian Exposition,* 1893 (no. 875);
Boston, Mass., Copley Hall, *Loan Collection of Portraits of Women,* 1895 (no. 257); Philadelphia,
Pennsylvania Academy of the Fine Arts, 1896; Boston, Mass., Copley Hall, *Paintings and Sketches by
John S. Sargent, R.A.,* Feb. 20-Mar. 13, 1899 (no. 5); Worcester, Mass., Worcester Art Museum, 1909;
Boston, Mass., Museum of Fine Arts, 1913 (no. 757), 1916 (no. 573), 1918 (no. 480), 1920 (no. 340), 1921
(no. 420), 1922 (no. 273); New York, Grand Central Art Galleries, *Retrospective Exhibition of Important
Works of John Singer Sargent,* Feb. 23-Apr. 6, 1924 (no. 20), repr. in cat. p. 45; New York, Metropolitan
Museum of Art, *Memorial Exhibition of the Works of John Singer Sargent,* Jan. 4-Feb. 14, 1926 (no. 26),
repr. in cat.; Boston, Mass., Museum of Fine Arts, 1928 (no. 168), 1929 (no. 993), 1930 (no. 530); Boston,
Mass., Museum of Fine Arts, centennial exhibition, *Sargent's Boston,* Jan. 3-Feb. 7, 1956 (no. 20); Los
Angeles County Museum of Art, Aug. 6-Dec. 9, 1974.

Armand Hammer Collection Exhibitions: see pp. 17-18.
First exhibited Memphis, 1969. Not exhibited Kansas City; New Orleans; Columbus; Little Rock;
Oklahoma City; San Diego; Los Angeles, 1974; Los Angeles, 1975; Moultrie.

Literature: Leila Mechlin, "The Sargent Exhibition," *American Magazine of Art,* vol. 15, no. 4 (Apr.
1924), pp. 169-90, repr. p. 184; Rose V. S. Berry, "John Singer Sargent: Some of His American Work," *Art
and Archaeology Throughout the Ages,* vol. 18, no. 3 (Sept. 1924), pp. 83-112, repr. p. 100; William Howe
Downes, *John S. Sargent, His Life and Work, Boston,* 1925, pp. 33, 157-58, repr. p. 128; Hon. Evan
Charteris, *John S. Sargent,* New York, 1927, pp. 109, 137, 263; Charles Merrill Mount, *John Singer
Sargent,* London, 1957, p. 153; David McKibbin, *Sargent's Boston,* catalogue, Museum of Fine Arts,
Boston, Mass., 1956, pp. 43, 68, 91, no. 20, repr. p. 41; *18th-20th Century American Paintings, etc.*
—*Various Owners,* sale catalogue, Parke-Bernet Galleries, Inc., New York, 1969, no. 74, repr.; Richard
Ormond, *John Singer Sargent: Paintings, Drawings, Watercolors,* New York, 1970, pp. 43, 246, repr.

Sargent's portrait of *Mrs. Edward L. Davis and
Her Son, Livingston Davis* is not a simple bust
portrait but an imposing composition demanding
the artist's full powers of invention and
execution. Sargent meets the challenge with
inspiration, and the figures of the
full-length double portrait spring to life
almost spontaneously.

The seemingly casual relationship between
the two figures is actually a relationship of
considerable formal and psychological

complexity. The precarious movement of the boy
contrasts with the monumentally stable
form of his mother, who looms forward as she
forcefully confronts the viewer. While the broad,
loose brushwork reflects Sargent's debt to the
Dutch and Spanish masters and, to an extent,
the Impressionists, the firm modeling and
dramatic lighting of the woman's head seem to
have something of the quality of the realist John
Singleton Copley, whose work Sargent discovered
in Boston.

L.C.

Thomas Eakins 1844-1916
b. Philadelphia   *d.* Philadelphia

59   *Portrait of Sebastiano Cardinal Martinelli,* 1902
Oil on canvas, mounted on panel 198.9 x 152.3 cm.
Signed and dated, lower right: *Eakins 1902*

Collection: Catholic University of America, Washington, D.C., presented by the artist in 1903 (sold Parke-Bernet Galleries, Inc., New York, May 21, 1970 (no. 57)).

Exhibitions: Pittsburgh, Museum of Art, Carnegie Institute, *International Exhibition,* 1903; Philadelphia, Pennsylvania Academy of the Fine Arts, *Thomas Eakins Memorial Exhibition,* Dec. 23, 1917-Jan. 23, 1918 (no. 20); Baltimore Museum of Art, *Thomas Eakins, A Retrospective Exhibition of His Paintings,* Dec. 1, 1936-Jan. 1, 1937 (no. 34); Philadelphia Museum of Art, *Thomas Eakins Centennial Exhibition,* 1944 (no. 99); Pittsburgh, Museum of Art, Carnegie Institute, *Thomas Eakins Centennial Exhibition,* Apr. 26-June 1, 1945 (no. 15), repr. in cat.; Washington, D.C., National Gallery of Art, 1969-70; Overbrook, Pa., Saint Charles Seminary, *Eakins Portraits,* 1970; New York, Whitney Museum of American Art, *Thomas Eakins Retrospective Exhibition,* Sept. 21-Nov. 29, 1970; Los Angeles County Museum of Art, Aug. 6-Dec. 9, 1974.

Armand Hammer Collection Exhibitions: see pp. 17-18.
First exhibited Kansas City, 1970. Not exhibited Los Angeles, 1974; Moultrie.

Literature: Lloyd Goodrich, *Thomas Eakins — His Life and Work,* New York, 1933, pp. 105-6, 194, no. 361; Fairfield Porter, *Thomas Eakins,* New York, 1959, fig. 64; Sylvan Schendler, *Thomas Eakins,* Boston, 1967, pp. 201, 208, 215, 296, plate 102; *Eighteenth, Nineteenth and Twentieth Century American Paintings,* sale catalogue, Parke-Bernet Galleries, Inc., New York, 1970, p. 58, no 57, repr. in color; Mahonri Sharp Young, "The Hammer Collection: Paintings," *Apollo,* vol. 95 (June 1972), p. 454, fig. 5.

As Lloyd Goodrich has pointed out, it seems paradoxical that Thomas Eakins, a Quaker and an uncompromising realist, should have begun in his late years a series of portraits of Catholic prelates. Seen as portraits of friends painted at the artist's own request, however, they begin to take their place very logically within his total oeuvre. Rejected as an artist and rather withdrawn from society, Eakins must have felt a close kinship with these learned men whose mission set them apart from the world.

As is often the case in Eakins' full-length portraits, this figure is placed at some distance from the viewer within a very real space, and the ambience eloquently conveys a feeling of solitary contemplation. This effect is further enhanced by the use of the profile view, which presents the figure as a hieratic image to be beheld without direct involvement of the spectator. From the casually rubbed earth color, suggesting wood paneling and parquet floor, to the subtle design of the rug, more or less monochromatic surroundings act as a foil, intensifying the impact of the cardinal's presence.

On September 16, 1903, Eakins wrote from 1729 Mount Vernon Street, Philadelphia, to the rector of The Catholic University of America:

Dear Sir:
I am the person who painted and presented to the University the full length portrait of Cardinal Martinelli.

I am solicited by the Carnegie Institute to exhibit specimens of my best work, and I should like to send there the Cardinal which has been exhibited in New York, Philadelphia and Chicago....

Please let me know promptly if the picture may be exhibited.

Yours truly,
(signed) Thomas Eakins

L.C.

Mary Cassatt 1844-1926
b. Allegheny City, Pennsylvania   *d.* Mesnil-Théribus, France

60   *Summertime,* 1894
Oil on canvas 73.4 x 100.0 cm.
Signed, lower right: *Mary Cassatt*

Collection: Huntington Hartford, New York (sold Parke-Bernet Galleries, Inc., New York,
May 10, 1971 (no. 28)).

Exhibitions: Baltimore Museum of Art, *Manet, Degas, Berthe Morisot and Mary Cassatt,* Apr. 18-June 3,
1962 (no. 116), lent by Huntington Hartford; St. Petersburg, Fla., Museum of Fine Arts, *Inaugural
Exhibition,* Feb. 7-Mar. 7, 1965 (no. 28), lent by Huntington Hartford; New York, M. Knoedler & Co.,
Mary Cassatt, Feb. 1-26, 1966 (no. 25), lent by Huntington Hartford; Southampton, N.Y., Parrish Art
Museum, *Miss Mary Cassatt, Paintings and the Graphic Arts,* July 30-Aug. 20, 1967 (no. 2), lent by
Huntington Hartford; Washington, D.C., National Gallery of Art, *Mary Cassatt,* Sept. 27-Nov. 8, 1970
(no. 55), lent by Huntington Hartford, p. 28 in cat., repr.; Washington, D.C., National Gallery of Art,
May 6-Aug. 12, 1973, New York, Whitney Museum of American Art, Sept. 18-Nov. 12, 1973; Cincinnati
Art Museum, Dec. 15, 1973-Jan. 31, 1974, and Raleigh, North Carolina Museum of Art, Mar. 8-Apr. 29,
1974, *American Impressionists Exhibition;* Los Angeles County Museum of Art, Aug. 6-Dec. 9, 1974;
Manila, National Museum of Manila, 1976.

Armand Hammer Collection Exhibitions: see pp. 17-18.
First exhibited Oklahoma City, 1971. Not exhibited Minsk; Riga; Odessa; Los Angeles, 1974;
Los Angeles, 1975.

Literature: Adelyn Dohme Breeskin, *Mary Cassatt, A Catalogue Raisonné of the Oils, Pastels,
Watercolors and Drawings,* Washington, D.C., 1970, p. 116, no. 240, repr.; Meryle Secrest, "The American
Impressionist, The Lyrical Mary Cassatt Goes on Exhibit in Washington," *Washington Post,* Sept. 20,
1970 (section K1), repr. in color; *Important Impressionist and Modern Paintings and Drawings,* sale
catalogue, Parke-Bernet Galleries, Inc., New York, 1971, p. 50, no. 28, repr. in color; Mahonri Sharp
Young, "The Hammer Collection: Paintings," *Apollo,* vol. 95 (June 1972), p. 454, repr. plate IX
in color p. 451.

Though Mary Cassatt's paintings are generally complex figure compositions, she remains essentially a portrait painter, concentrating on the likeness and character of individuals. As a rule, even when she painted figures engaged in some activity out-of-doors, she was as much concerned with portraiture as with the disposition of form and features within a pictorial space. Among the few exceptions are three boating scenes from 1893-94 (Breeskin, nos. 230, 233, and 240, the present work). In none of these are the subjects identified, but in the famous *The Boating Party (near Antibes),* 1893, the personalities emerge with great strength. In the other two, which are closely related, the identity of the figures is not an important factor, and the intention seems to be simply the creation of a plein-air view of people in a boat observing or feeding ducks.

A number of important factors entered into the conception of *Summertime.* As early as 1890, Cassatt had resolved to concentrate on strengthening form and drawing, much as Renoir did in mid-career, and the following year a series of prints emulating the Japanese had a profound effect on her style. This is obvious in *The Boating Party,* but while boldness of design is still very important in *Summertime,* it is augmented by a system of slashing, dynamic brushwork verging on abstraction. Interestingly, the large allegory commissioned for the Chicago World's Fair and painted in 1892 also included women and ducks in a landscape.

L.C.

Maurice Brazil Prendergast 1861-1924
b. Saint John's, Newfoundland   *d.* New York

61   *On the Beach,* 1916
      Oil on canvas 67.9 x 99.0 cm.

Collections: Mrs. Charles Prendergast, Westport, Conn.; Lester Avnet, New York; A.C.A.
Galleries, New York.

Exhibitions: Pittsburgh, Museum of Art, Carnegie Institute, *Twenty-third Annual International
Exhibition of Paintings,* Apr. 24-June 15, 1924 (no. 14); Hartford, Conn., Wadsworth Atheneum,
Connecticut Collections, Oct. 1957; Stamford, Conn., Stamford Museum and Nature Center, Nov. 1961;
New York, A.C.A. Galleries, *Lester Avnet Collection,* Sept. 18-Oct. 18, 1969; Los Angeles County
Museum of Art, Aug. 6-Dec. 9, 1974.

Armand Hammer Collection Exhibitions: see pp. 17-18.
First exhibited Little Rock, 1970-71. Not exhibited Los Angeles, 1974; Lima; Los Angeles, 1975; Moultrie.

Literature: *Catalogue of the Twenty-third Annual International Exhibition of Paintings,* Carnegie
Institute, Pittsburgh, 1924, no. 14.

Unlike many of his contemporaries, Prendergast
did not embrace the more conservative aspects of
Impressionism. Rather, from the beginning, he
struck out in a direction close to that of the Post-
Impressionists and the Nabis. Later, there were
even stylistic parallels with the Fauves.

   Typical of Prendergast's later painting in oil,
this work exhibits nothing of the realist doctrine
generally associated with other members of The
Eight group. His subjects were not the crowded
streets of the New York slums painted by the
Ashcan School but groups of happy people at
their leisure on the beach, in the park, thronging
the sunny boulevards of Paris or the bridges of
Venice. Figures are generally disposed laterally
across the foreground against highly simplified
forms of sea and land. The ultimate result is
a bright, lyrical tapestry of color with shapes
loosely defined by a heavy line breaking or
fading against shifting planes of color as it
approximates contour.

                                            L.C.

Frederic Remington 1861-1909
b. Canton, Ohio   *d.* New York

*112   *Cowpuncher's Lullaby*, ca. 1906
Oil on canvas 76.2 x 53.5 cm.
Signed, lower right: *Frederic Remington*

Collection: Private collection, United States.

Armand Hammer Collection Exhibitions: see pp. 17-18.
First exhibited Washington, D.C., 1980.

Frederic Remington is recognized as foremost among artists who documented the early American West. Extremely prolific and fascinated by every detail of frontier life, Remington portrayed in drawing, painting and sculpture that rich period in America's history. Remington began his career as an illustrator and it was not until the last six years of his life that he devoted his time to easel painting.

Moonlight scenes or nocturnes are rare in Remington's work and they tended to be monochromatic—with the exception of

Cowpuncher's Lullaby. This painting is a departure from Remington's other nocturnes in the choice of colors used to create moonlight effects. It can be considered one of Remington's finest works.

The painting represents a practice in the early days when cattle herds fed on the open range. They were vulnerable, particularly at night, to attacks by Indians or white rustlers. Cattle had to be rounded up and guarded by night herders who frequently sang to them to prevent sudden stampedes.

H.McC.

*Recent acquisition

158

Charles Marion Russell 1856-1926
b. St. Louis, Missouri   *d.* Great Falls, Montana

*113   *The War Party*
Oil on canvas 55.9 x 91.4 cm.
Signed, lower left: *CM Russell* with skull insignia

Collections: Cowboy Hall of Fame, Oklahoma City, Oklahoma; Ward A. McGinnis, Eldorado, Kansas; Private collection.

Armand Hammer Collection Exhibitions: see pp. 17-18.
First exhibited Washington, D.C., 1980.

Literature: "Russell's West Remains," *Kansas City Star*, December 12, 1926, p. 25, repr. in color; *The Cattleman* (October 1952), repr. in color on cover; *Parker County Texas Frontier Days Souvenir Program*, 1955, repr. in color on cover; Karl Yost, *Charles M. Russell The Cowboy Artist a Bibliography*, (Pasadena: Trail's End Publishing Co., 1948), p. 134, no. 43; Karl Yost & Frederic G. Renner, *A Bibliography of the Published Works of Charles M. Russell* (Omaha: University of Nebraska Press, 1971), repr. in color facing p. 186.

The War Party by Charles Marion Russell is a classic subject particularly familiar to this artist. He spent much time in intimate association with the colorful and warlike Blackfeet Indians whose territory included northern Montana and Canada just across the border. No artist was better informed than Russell of the battles fought by these Indians with their traditional tribal enemies. He became widely known as the Montana cowboy artist and is today popularly recognized—as is Remington—as one of the foremost pictorial documentarians of the early American West.

H.McC.

*Recent acquisition

Drawings, Pastels and Watercolors

Albrecht Dürer 1471-1528
b. Nuremburg, Germany   *d.* Nuremburg

62   *Tuft of Cowslips,* 1526
     Gouache on vellum   19.2 x 16.8 cm.
     Inscribed (in a later hand): *AD 1526*

Collections: Priv. coll., England; Hal O'Nians, London.

Exhibitions: Washington, D.C., National Gallery of Art, *Recent Acquisitions and Promised Gifts,*
June 2-Sept. 1, 1974 (no. 66); Washington, D.C., National Gallery of Art, *Master Drawings from the
Collection of the National Gallery of Art and Promised Gifts,* June 1978 (no. 23).

Armand Hammer Collection Exhibitions: see pp. 17-18.
First exhibited Los Angeles, 1971-72. Not exhibited Los Angeles, 1974; Los Angeles, 1975; Moultrie.

Literature: Otto Benesch, *Master Drawings in the Albertina,* New York, 1967, p. 337; Charles W. Talbot,
ed., G. Ravenel, and J. Levenson, *Dürer in America — His Graphic Work,* New York, 1971, p. 110, note 3;
The Armand Hammer Collection, Los Angeles, 1971, no. 60; Walter Koschatzky and Alice Strobl,
Graphische Sammlung Albertina, die Dürerzeichnungen der Albertina zum 500. Geburtstag, Vienna,
1971, no. 28; Christopher White, "The Armand Hammer Collection: Drawings," *Apollo,* vol. 95 (June
1972), pp. 457-58, fig. 2; Alan Shestack, "Dürer's Graphic Work in Washington and Boston," *Art
Quarterly,* vol. 35 (1972), p. 304; John Rowlands, Review of *Albrecht Dürer: 1471-1971* and *Dürer in
America, Master Drawings,* vol. 10, 1972, p. 384; Walter L. Strauss, *The Complete Drawings of Albrecht
Dürer,* New York, 1974, vol. 2, p. 726, no. 1503/37, repr. p. 727, as Dürer about 1503; *Recent Acquisitions
and Promised Gifts,* catalogue, National Gallery of Art, Washington, D.C., 1974, no. 66; Jaro Springer,
"Dürers Zeichnungen in neuen Publikationen," *Repertorium für Kunstwissenschaft,* vol. 29 (1906),
pp. 555 ff.; Joseph Meder, "Die grüne Passion und die Tier-und Pflanzenstudien Albrecht Dürers in der
Albertina," Repertorium für Kunstwissenschaft, vol. 30 (1907), p. 181; Sebastian Killermann, *A. Dürers
Pflanzen und Tierzeichnungen, Studien zur deutschen Kunstgeschichte,* vol. 119, Strassburg, 1910,
pp. 94ff.; Friedrich Winkler, *Die Zeichnungen Albrecht Dürers,* Berlin, 1936, vol. 2, pp. 65ff.; Heinrich
Schwartz, "A Water-colour Attributed to Dürer," *Burlington Magazine,* vol. 95 (1953), pp. 149ff.; Hans
Kauffmann, "Dürer in der Kunst und im Kunsturteil um 1600," *Anzeiger des Germanischen
Nationalmuseums in Nürnberg, 1940-53,* Berlin, 1954, p. 29.

Albrecht Dürer
Tuft of Cowslips, detail

The *Tuft of Cowslips* is one of a group of plant studies by Dürer, most of which are now in the Graphische Sammlung Albertina, Vienna, having come there from the collection of Emperor Rudolf II in Prague (*see* Koschatzky and Strobl, nos. 27-32. For the whole group, *see* the works cited above by Joseph Meder, Sebastian Killermann, Friedrich Winkler, and Charles W. Talbot, ed. (pp. 108-10)). The most celebrated of these sheets is the *Large Piece of Turf,* which was drawn on paper in watercolor with some touches of gouache; it bears the date 1503. Other drawings in the group, such as the *Columbine,* the *Celandine,* and the *Three Medicinal Herbs,* are executed on vellum, mostly in a smooth and opaque gouache. The small *Nosegay of Violets,* though also in gouache on vellum, is somewhat freer in style than the works of this latter group.

Although Jaro Springer categorically doubted the authenticity of all the animal and plant studies ascribed to Dürer, the *Large Piece of Turf* has always been accepted as an original, while the drawings on vellum have often been doubted (recently again by Alan Shestack and John Rowlands, who also rejected the Hammer sheet). It has been suggested that they might be by an imitator of Dürer of around 1600, such as Hans Hoffmann, but Professor Hans Kauffmann had correctly repudiated this thesis, explaining clearly the differences between these later imitations and genuine early

sixteenth century works.

The recent catalogue of Dürer's drawings in the Albertina and the latest monograph on Dürer's drawings by Walter Strauss, have defended the authenticity of the group of plant studies on vellum, and the Hammer sheet actually helps to support this attribution. (Firm supporters of the Hammer sheet were Otto Benesch and recently Walter Koschatzky and Alice Strobl, all of whom were able to examine the sheet in the Albertina.) *The Tuft of Cowslips* is related to these drawings in general type and technique; it also bears the inscribed date of 1526 that appears on other sheets in the group. The inscription is surely the addition of a collector who at one time owned them all. When the Hammer drawing was taken to the Albertina to be studied in 1971, it became clear that the color was much more lively in application and more transparent than it was in the other works on vellum. In fact, the highly differentiated greens corresponded almost exactly to those of the *Large Piece of Turf,* while their loose application resembled that in the leaves of the *Nosegay of Violets.* Although the *Tuft of Cowslips* does not show the linear qualities typical of most of Dürer's plant studies on paper, it does parallel the *Large Piece of Turf* in its spatial depth, in the richness of the observation of light, and in the sense of life that seems to emanate from the plant.

K.O.

Leonardo da Vinci 1452-1519
b. Anchiano, Italy   *d.* Clos-Lucé, France

63   *Sheet of Studies*
Head of an old man in right profile; two detailed studies of the right eye; bust of a woman from three-quarter rear with head in right profile; bust of a girl from three-quarter rear with head turned toward viewer. Pen and brown ink over traces of black chalk (recto)

Study of a Madonna (verso)
Black chalk 16.4 x 13.8 cm.

Watermark: tulip, close to Charles Moïse Briquet, *Les filigranes: dictionnaire historique des marques du papier,* Geneva, 1907, vol. 2, nos. 6645-59.

Collection: P. & D. Colnaghi & Co., Ltd., London.

Exhibitions: Washington, D.C., National Gallery of Art, *Recent Acquisitions and Promised Gifts,* June 2-Sept. 1, 1974 (no. 65); Los Angeles County Museum of Art, *Old Master Drawings from American Collections,* Apr. 29-June 13, 1976; Washington, D.C., National Gallery of Art, *Master Drawings from the Collection of the National Gallery of Art and Promised Gifts,* June 1978 (no. 32), Washington, D.C., January 17-January 25, 1981.

Armand Hammer Collection Exhibitions: see pp. 17-18.
First exhibited Dublin, 1972. Not exhibited Los Angeles, 1974; Moultrie; West Palm Beach; Cincinnati.

Literature: *The Armand Hammer Collection,* Los Angeles, 1971, no. 104; *Recent Acquisitions and Promised Gifts,* catalogue, National Gallery of Art, Washington, D.C., 1974, no. 65.

This drawing, accepted by Sir Kenneth Clark as an original work of Leonardo, is a fragment of a large sheet surely once the size of the study for a *Virgin, the Christ Child, and Saint John* in Windsor Castle. The Hammer drawing is on similar paper in the same color ink and may have been done at the same time in the artist's life, in the 1470s. Typical for Leonardo are the scattered sketches, prominent among them the profile head of the middle-aged man with a large nose and chin and intense gaze, of a type found also on the Windsor sheet, but without the beard (see A. E. Popham, *The Drawings of Leonardo da Vinci,* London, 1946, nos. 22-24, 27; Kenneth Clark and Carlo Pedretti, *The Drawings of Leonardo da Vinci in the Collection of Her Majesty the Queen at Windsor Castle,* London, 1968, no. 12276). Close by we find the same face studied from the front, with special emphasis on the eye, and the study of this eye from yet another point of view. Below there are two busts of women. The larger one is definitely connected with another sheet in Windsor Castle where Leonardo used the silverpoint to draw busts of women seen from many different directions (Clark and Pedretti, no. 12513; Popham, no. 22). Both A. E. Popham and Kenneth Clark recognized the relationship between this drawing and the larger Windsor sheet with the study of the Madonna. The smaller bust below on the Hammer sheet with its lively movement and

spirited gaze directed at the spectator, drawn with a fresh and fluidly curling stroke that characterizes the puffy sleeve, is extremely close to the study of a maiden with a unicorn in the British Museum (Popham, no. 27), of which there is another version in the Ashmolean Museum in Oxford, both surely drawn at the same time. John Walker had already pointed out the resemblance of the Oxford drawing to the portrait of *Ginevra de' Benci* in the National Gallery of Art in Washington, D.C. (John Walker, "Ginevra de' Benci by Leonardo da Vinci," *Report and Studies in the History of Art,* National Gallery of Art, Washington, D.C., 1967, p. 20, fig. 19). David Brown very convincingly suggested (in correspondence) that Leonardo may indeed have planned this subject, a symbol of virtue and virginity, for the back of that portrait instead of the more abstract plant symbols that adorn it now. He is also right in proposing that the studies of female busts are indeed drawn in search of the pose of that portrait.

The slight sketches on the back of the sheet are difficult to read. Next to some studies of legs and a torso, the main subject seems to be the Virgin, but no definite relationship to extant studies of works by Leonardo can be found. The drawing style, however, is clearly his and is typical of the slight sketches in metalpoint or black chalk found on many of his sheets.

K.O.

168

Michelangelo Buonarroti 1475-1564
b. Caprese, Italy   *d.* Rome

64   *Male Nude,* ca. 1560 (recto)
      Black chalk 23.3 x 10.0 cm.

Collections: Sir J. C. Robinson, Swanage; John Malcolm, Poltalloch; the Hon. A. E. Gathorne-Hardy, London; Geoffrey Gathorne-Hardy, Newberry, Berkshire; the Hon. Robert Gathorne-Hardy, Stanford Dingley, Berkshire.

Exhibitions: London, British Museum, *An Exhibition of Drawings by Michelangelo Belonging to H. M. the Queen, the Ashmolean Museum, the British Museum and Other English Collections,* Apr. 15-June 28, 1953 (no. 128); Manchester, City Art Gallery, *Between Renaissance and Baroque: European Art 1520-1600,* Mar. 10-Apr. 6, 1965 (no. 338); London, P. & D. Colnaghi & Co., Ltd., Oct. 12-Nov. 5, 1971, and Oxford, Ashmolean Museum, Nov. 20, 1971-Jan. 2, 1972, *Loan Exhibition of Drawings by Old Masters from the Collection of Mr. Geoffrey Gathorne-Hardy* (no. 9), plate VII in cat.; London, British Museum, *Drawings by Michelangelo,* 1975 (no. 156); London, Sotheby & Co., *Old Master Drawings from the Gathorne-Hardy Collection,* Apr. 28, 1976 (no. 14), repr. in cat.; Los Angeles, Los Angeles County Museum of Art, *Old Master Drawings from American Collections,* Apr. 29-June 13, 1976; Washington, D.C., National Gallery of Art, *Master Drawings from the Collection of the National Gallery of Art and Promised Gifts,* June 1978 (no. 40).

Armand Hammer Collection Exhibitions: see pp. 17-18.
First exhibited Nashville, 1976. Not exhibited Moultrie.

Literature: *Descriptive Catalogue of Drawings...in the Possession of the Hon. A. E. Gathorne-Hardy,* London, 1902, no. 7; Bernard Berenson, *The Drawings of the Florentine Painters,* New York, 1903, vol. 2, no. 1540; Henry Thode, *Michelangelo: kritische Untersuchungen über seine Werke,* Berlin, 1913, p. 163, no. 368; Bernard Berenson, *The Drawings of the Florentine Painters,* Chicago, 1938, vol. 2, no. 1544b, fig. 717; Johannes Wilde, *Italian Drawings...in the British Museum, Michelangelo and His Studio,* London, 1953, p. 116, no. 75; Luitpold Dussler, *Die Zeichnungen des Michelangelo,* Berlin, 1959, no. 338, plate 136; Charles de Tolnay, *Michelangelo, the Final Period,* Princeton, N.J., 1960, p. 206, no. 219, plate 197; Bernard Berenson, *I disegni dei pittori fiorentini,* Milan, 1961, vol. 2, no. 1544b; Frederick Hartt, *The Drawings of Michelangelo,* London, 1971, p. 352, as Michelangelo of 1546, p. 357, no. 509 recto, repr.; John Gere and Nicholas Turner, *Drawings by Michelangelo,* catalogue, British Museum, London, 1975, no. 156, repr.; Paul Joannides, "Review of the Exhibition 'Drawings by Michelangelo' at the British Museum," *Burlington Magazine,* vol. 117 (1975), p. 262.

Male Nude, ca. 1560 (verso)
Black chalk 23.3 x 10.0 cm.

In his last years, Michelangelo synthesized two subjects that had occupied him in earlier periods — Christ being carried to the tomb and a presentation of his body. Christ is transported in such a manner that his body is fully and frontally displayed to the beholder. On a sheet in the Ashmolean Museum (Hartt, no. 459), the artist had twice slightly but movingly sketched such a composition: two men are supporting Christ's body on either side with their shoulders and hands. To the left and right of these sketches the artist varied the motif: the body is held by either the Virgin or Joseph of Arimathea alone, as the artist sculpted it in the *Pietà Rondanini* in Milan. The central sketches were therefore regarded by some authors, such as John Gere and Nicholas Turner (*Drawings,* p. 132), as the "germ of the *Pietà.*" Recently, however, Paul Joannides realized that Michelangelo further pursued the idea of showing Christ supported by two men. Both the Hammer drawing and several sketches in the Ashmolean Museum testify to this theory. The somewhat static stance of the figures in the earlier Ashmolean sketch was transformed by Michelangelo in these studies into more emphatic forward movement. He gave a greater flexibility to the legs and a stronger

bent and power to the torsos and shoulders.

The two studies on recto and verso of the Hammer sheet are important to this process. The drawing on the verso is lightly traced through from the front and shows that Michelangelo was experimenting here with the placement of this figure at either the left or the right of Christ in an essentially symmetrical composition. The sheets in the Ashmolean show the same preoccupation, presenting the figure with and without drapery. As Joannides pointed out, a drawing by a follower of Michelangelo, once with the Hammer sheet in the Gathorne-Hardy Collection (sold Sotheby, Apr. 28, 1976, no. 15), preserves the results of Michelangelo's studies: here, the figure from the Hammer sheet is employed at the left of Christ, but it shows, in accordance with the Oxford studies, greater forward movement and ecstatic features. Christ no longer rests on the man's shoulders; instead, the man carries the Savior's torso and legs, as does his companion on the right. Two more figures behind support Christ's upper arms.

According to Joannides, architectural sketches on one of the Ashmolean drawings point to a date of about 1560 for these studies.

K.O.

Raphael 1483-1520
b. Urbino, Italy   *d.* Urbino

65   *Study for a Fresco of the Prophets Hosea and Jonah*
Pen and brown wash, heightened with white, over preparation in black chalk and stylus, squared with
stylus and red chalk 27.0 x 19.8 cm.

Collections: Jonathan Richardson, Sr. (1665-1745); London; Jonathan Richardson, Jr., London (Lugt,
(Frits Lugt, *Les Marques de collections, de dessins & d'estampes,* Amsterdam, 1921), no. 2170));
P. J. Mariette, Paris (Lugt, no. 2097); H. C. Jennings, London (Lugt, no. 2771); R. Payne Knight,
London (Lugt, no. 1577; Baron H. de Triquety, Paris (Lugt, no. 1304)); E. Colando, Paris (Lugt, no. 837);
Major S. V. Christie-Miller, C.B.E. Salisbury; P. & D., Colnaghi & Co., Ltd., London.

Exhibitions: Washington, D.C. National Gallery of Art, *Recent Acquisitions and Promised Gifts,*
June 2-Sept. 1, 1974 (no. 67); Los Angeles County Museum of Art, *Old Master Drawings from American
Collections,* Apr. 29-June 13, 1976, repr. in cat.; Washington, D.C., National Gallery of Art, *Master
Drawings from the Collection of the National Gallery of Art and Promised Gifts,* June 1978 (no. 36).

Armand Hammer Collection Exhibitions: see pp. 17-18.
First exhibited Los Angeles, 1971-72. Not exhibited Los Angeles, 1974; Los Angeles, 1975; Moultrie.

Literature: Jonathan Richardson, *An Account of the Statues, Bas-Reliefs, Drawings and Pictures in
Italy, France, etc., with Remarks by Mr. Richardson, Sen. and Jun.* (2nd ed.), London, 1754, p. 104;
C. Metz, *Imitations of Ancient and Modern Drawings,* London, 1798, plate 44; F. A. Gruyer, *Raphael et
l'antiquité,* Paris, 1846, vol. 1, p. 379, no. 1; J. D. Passavant, *Raphaël d'Urbin,* Paris, 1860, vol. 2, p. 142;
C. Ruland, *The Works of Raphael Santi da Urbino as Represented in the Raphael Collection in the
Royal Library at Windsor Castle,* London, 1876, p. 271, section III; J. A. Crowe and G. B. Cavalcaselle,
Raphael, Life and Works, London, 1882-85, vol. 2, p. 216, note; G. E. Lafenstre and E. Richtenberger,
Rome, le Vatican et les églises, Paris, 1903, p. 263; Oskar Fishel, "Some Lost Drawings by or near
Raphael." *Burlington Magazine,* vol. 20 (1912), p. 299, plate II, fig. 12, Oskar Fishel, "Santi," in Thieme-
Becker, *Allgemeines Lexikon der Bildenden Künstler,* vol. 29, Leipzig, 1935, p. 438; Oskar Fishel,
Raphael, a Critical Catalogue of His Pictures, Wall-Paintings and Tapestries, London 1971, p. 94; *The
Armand Hammer Collection,* Los Angeles, 1971, no. 61; Christopher White, "The Armand Hammer
Collection: Drawings," *Apollo,* vol. 95 (June 1972), p. 457, fig. 1, p. 456; *Recent Acquisitions and
Promised Gifts,* catalogue, National Gallery of Art, Washington, D.C., 1975, no. 67.

Raphael
Study for a Fresco of the Prophets Hosea and Jonah, detail

This drawing, highly regarded in the eighteenth and nineteenth centuries and possessed by some of the finest collectors of the time (among them the great connoisseur, P. J. Mariette) disappeared from view in the beginning of the twentieth century, and has since been known only from old photographs. The views expressed by Oskar Fischel and Luitpold Dussler that the sheet could be by a pupil must be regarded in this light.

James Byam Shaw, who rediscovered the sheet, clearly recognized its great value. It is a preparatory drawing for the two figures of prophets at the left of the window high above the ground in the Chigi Chapel in Santa Maria della Pace in Rome, painted by Raphael probably in 1511. As the figures in the fresco have lost much by restoration, the drawing is of special value. Raphael must already have made a number of sketches for these prophets when he drew this sheet. He first squared the sheet with a stylus to have a grid that could facilitate the drawing of the figures to exact scale. Then he drew them in with black chalk and pen. While the ink was still partially wet, he washed in the shadows with large, rapid touches of the brush and then added the white highlights. The angel between the two

was sketched in with the stylus and then with the pen in a much more rapid fashion, after having been placed in a quite different position in an early sketch (*see* Michael Hirst, "The Chigi Chapel in S. Maria della Pace," *Journal of the Warburg and Courtauld Institutes,* vol. 24, (1961), especially fig. 28c; *see also* Fischel, *Raphael,* vol. 2, fig. 193).

Raphael seems to have reconsidered the angel's pose and place on this sheet, which also explains why it is drawn in the nude; such was Raphael's habit in order to define more clearly a figure's position. He then covered the sheet with another grid in red chalk, probably to transfer the design directly to the full-scale cartoon for the fresco. Parallels for the drawing style of this sheet, both for the finished and for the rapidly drawn portions, can be found among the studies for the *Parnassus,* painted close in time to the prophets. Parallels for the figure style can be found in the *School of Athens* of about 1510. Influences from Donatello and Michelangelo are clearly discernible, especially in the fierce expression of the seated prophet, Hosea.

K.O.

Andrea del Sarto 1486-1530
b. Florence   *d.* Florence

66   *Female Head*
Black chalk 32.7 x 22.5 cm., the top corners cut
Signed, lower left recto, pen and ink: *A. Del Sarto*
Signed, lower left verso, red chalk, twice: *Andrea del Sarto*

Collections: Jan Pietcrsz, Zoomer (1641-1724), Amsterdam (Lugt (Frits Lugt, *Les Marques de collections, de dessins & d'estampes,* Amsterdam, 1921), no. 1511); Jonathan Richardson, Sr. (1665-1745), London (Lugt, nos. 2183 and 2184); fifth duke of Argyll, by 1784; T. Philipe's Sale, London, May 21-23, 1798; Walter Savage Landor, Florence; priv. coll., Zurich.

Armand Hammer Collection Exhibitions: see pp. 17-18.
First exhibited Malibu, 1977. Not exhibited Moultrie.

Literature: John Shearman, *Andrea del Sarto,* Oxford, 1965, pp. 385-86, p. 289, no. 3, plate 47a.

At one time, John Shearman was not convinced of the authenticity of this drawing; however, after seeing the original he accepted it as an autographed work of the highest quality. Sydney Freedberg and Konrad Oberhuber concur. Shearman believes the Hammer drawing may be a study from life for Andrea's *Borghese Madonna* of about 1516 and could have been used a year earlier by one of his assistants for the *Madonna* at Ottawa. The drawing differs from the Borghese painting only in the eyes and the headpiece and is almost identical in form and expression to the Ottawa *Madonna.* The very unconventional V-shaped composition drawing (Uffizi Gall., no. 304) that was used in its entirety for the Borghese picture lacks a finished study for the head. Another female figure closely resembling the Hammer study, and of the same date, appears to the left of the preaching Saint John the Baptist in Andrea's fresco at the Chiostro dello Scalzo, Florence, of 1515.

The provenance of the Hammer drawing indicates its importance. By 1690 it had found its way into the hands of J. P. Zoomer, one of the most knowlegeable art dealers of the seventeenth century, and from there it went into the collection of Jonathan Richardson, Sr., a great connoisseur and collector of Italian drawings.

M.E.

R

A Del Sarto.

Antonio Allegri da Correggio 1489 or 1494-1534
b. Correggio, Italy   *d.* Correggio

67   *Study for the "Madonna Della Scodella"* (recto)
Red chalk, pen and brush in brown ink
22.0 x 14.0 cm.

*Study for a Fresco of Saint Matthew
and Saint Jerome* (verso)
Red chalk, pen and brush in brown ink
21.0 x 14.0 cm.

Collections: Sir Peter Lely, London (Lugt (Frits Lugt, *Les Marques de collections, de dessins, &
d'estampes,* Amsterdam, 1921), no. 2092); P. & D. Colnaghi & Co., Ltd., London, Michael Hirst, London.

Exhibitions: Edinburgh, Merchants Hall, Arts Council of Great Britain in association with the
Edinburgh Festival Society, *Exhibition of Italian 16th Century Drawings from British Private
Collections,* Aug. 23-Sept. 13, 1969 (no. 30); Washington, D.C., National Gallery of Art, *Recent
Acquisitions and Promised Gifts,* June 2-Sept. l, 1974 (no. 68).

Armand Hammer Collection Exhibitions: see pp. 17-18.
First exhibited San Francisco, 1971. Not exhibited San Diego; Kiev; Los Angeles, 1974; Los Angeles,
1975; Moultrie.

Literature: *Italian 16th Century Drawings from British Private Collections,* catalogue, Arts Council of
Great Britain in association with the Edinburgh Festival Society, Merchants Hall, Edinburgh, 1969,
no. 30; Konrad Oberhuber, "Drawings by Artists working in Parma in the Sixteenth Century." *Master
Drawings,* vol. 8 (1970), pp. 278-79, plates 30, 31; *The Armand Hammer Collection,* Los Angeles, 1971,
no. 62; Christopher White, "The Armand Hammer Collection: Drawings," *Apollo,* vol. 95 (June 1972),
p. 458, figs. 3, 4; Robert Hodge, "Three Stages in the Genesis of Correggio's Madonna della Scodella,"
Burlington Magazine, vol. 95 (1973), pp. 603-6; *Recent Acquisitions and Promised Gifts,* catalogue,
National Gallery of Art, Washington, D.C., 1974, no. 68.

In Correggio's drawings, the disposition of light
and shade is primarily responsible for creating
the shape and volume of the figures. Forms are
evoked rather than delineated, and there is a
sense of limitless possibility in the figures'
movements. The recto of the Hammer collection
drawing contains an unusually complete but still
quite free design for the famous *Madonna della
Scodella,* painted in 1529-30 and now in the
Pinacoteca at Parma. This rapid sketch may be
earlier, perhaps 1523-24, the date of the earliest
surviving documents of the commission for the
painting. Both the figures and the style of
drawing correspond more closely to Correggio's
works of that time.

There is a copy in Windsor Castle of a lost
drawing by Correggio, recently recognized by
Robert Hodge, which makes it clear that the
artist must have been working intensely on the
Madonna della Scodella at that earlier date. Like
the Hammer drawing, this sheet reflects the
style of Correggio's frescoes in San Giovanni
Evangelista in Parma, then in progress, and
shows that for this new project he looked back to

his own earlier compositions, the *Rest on the
Flight into Egypt,* in the Uffizi Gallery or the
Mystic Marriage of Saint Catherine, in Naples.
The lost drawing, of which the Windsor sheet
is a copy, must have been contemporary with
Correggio's *Noli me tangere,* in the Prado. Both
the Hammer collection drawing and the lost
original of the Windsor drawing seem, therefore,
to have been done in the same period. The style
of this lost original can be compared to the brush
drawings made by Correggio for the frieze in the
nave of San Giovanni Evangelista and for the
Del Bono Chapel in the same church (see
A. E. Popham, *Correggio's Drawings,* London,
1957, nos. 37 and 44).

On the verso of our drawing, there is actually
a study for one of the pendentives of the dome
of San Giovanni Evangelista. It is the earliest
known design for the *Saints Matthew and
Jerome,* for which other studies are preserved
in Munich and London (Popham, *Correggio's
Drawings,* nos. 17 and 18; Popham nos. 19
and 20 in the Uffizi and in the Conte Raisini
Collection in Milan show a more finished design).

K.O.

Rembrandt van Rijn 1606-1669
b. Leiden, Holland   *d.* Amsterdam

68   *Study of a Beggar Man and Woman*
Pen and brown ink 12.7 x 11 cm.

Collections: Jonathan Richardson, Sr., London (Lugt (Frits Lugt, *Les Marques de collections, de dessins, & d'estampes,* Amsterdam, 1921), no. 2183); Sir Joshua Reynolds, London (Lugt, no. 2364); Sir Thomas Lawrence, London (Lugt, no. 2445); William Esdaile (Lugt, no. 2617; sold Christie's London, June 17, 1840 (lot 4), bought by Sheath); Sir Archibald Campbell, Bt., Argyllshire; by descent to Sir Ilay Campbell, Bt., Argyllshire.

Armand Hammer Collection Exhibitions: see pp. 17-18.
First exhibited Paris, 1977. Not exhibited Moultrie.

Literature: A. M. Hind, *Vasari Society,* 1908-9, ser. 1, pt. IV, no. 26; Kurt Bauch, *Die Kunst des jungen Rembrandts,* 1933, pp. 114-18, 204-5, fig. III; Otto Benesch, *The Drawings of Rembrandt,* London, 1954, vol. 2, no. 206, fig. 223, (2nd ed., 1973, fig. 241.)

From his earliest days in Leiden, Rembrandt seems to have made a practice of drawing scenes from everyday life. His reliance on nature was commented on by such early biographers as Joachim von Sandrart. It is not, however, entirely clear whether the two figures in this drawing, a beggar man and woman in the street, were studied independently or seen together in a mute dialogue. The man turns away from the woman toward the right, while she veers to the left with arms outstretched. The depiction of shadows on the figures and on the ground from the same light source suggests the manner of the early etching of a *Beggar Man and Woman in Conversation* (Johann Adam Bernhard von Bartsch, *Le Peintre graveur,* no. 164), dated 1630.

There has been some discussion as to exactly when this drawing was made. Whereas Kurt Bauch believed that it was executed about 1630, while Rembrandt was still in Leiden, Otto Benesch was of the opinion that the angular style of drawing indicated a slightly later date, about 1632-33, after the artist's move to Amsterdam. Benesch based his opinion on a comparison of the Hammer drawing with *Christ Conversing with Martha and Mary* (Benesch, no. 79), in the Teylers Museum, Haarlem, which is characteristic of Rembrandt's early Amsterdam studies. Following the development of his drawing style from the early *Beggar Couple with a Dog,* ca. 1628-29 (executed in the manner of Jacques Callot's etchings) Rembrandt brought more characterization to each head and reduced obvious contrasts of light and shade, both features of the present work. On the other hand, comparison with "late" Leiden etchings, when the artist was concerned with beggar subjects, suggests that Benesch's dating may be marginally too late. Apart from theme, the Hammer drawing has much in common with the *Beggar Man and Woman in Conversation,* of 1630. Perhaps fortuitously, the turned pose of the man, with hands behind his back, recurs in the *Ragged Peasant* (Bartsch, no. 172), of about 1630. The woman reappears, in reverse, in the background of the etching of the *Blind Fiddler* (Bartsch, no. 138), dated 1631.

C.W.

Rembrandt van Rijn 1606-1669

69   *A Biblical Subject*
Pen and ink, brown wash, heightened with white 17.3 x 17.2 cm.
Watermark: Arms of Amsterdam.

Collection: B. F. Nicholson (sold Sotheby & Co., London, Mar. 23, 1971 (no. 90)).

Exhibitions: Washington, D.C., National Gallery of Art, *Recent Acquisitions and Promised Gifts,*
June 2-Sept. 1, 1974 (no. 69); Los Angeles County Museum of Art, *Old Master Drawings from
American Collections,* Apr. 29-June 13, 1976.

Armand Hammer Collection Exhibitions: see pp. 17-18.
First exhibited Oklahoma City, 1971. Not exhibited San Diego; Los Angeles, 1974; Los Angeles,
1975; Moultrie.

Literature: Christopher White, "The Hammer Collection: Drawings," *Apollo,* vol. 95 (June 1972),
pp. 458-60, fig. 5.

An elderly king, wearing a turban surmounted by
a crown, and holding a scepter in his right hand,
is seated on a throne beneath a baldachino. On
the right, two female figures kneel side by side
before him. The woman on the left clasps
something on her knee.

The king is similar in type to the artist's
representation of biblical kings, as, for example,
David in the drawing of *Nathan Admonishing
David* (about 1655), in the Metropolitan Museum
of Art (see Otto Benesch, *The Drawings of
Rembrandt,* London, 1954-57, vol 5. no, 948). He
also bears a strong affinity to a number of the
figures in the copies Rembrandt made after
Moghul miniatures in the mid-1650s (Benesch,
nos. 1187-1206), suggesting that the artist drew
inspiration from these for his representation of
an Old Testament figure.

The 1971 sale catalogue suggests that the
subject might depict the *Judgment of Solomon,*
but this is not entirely convincing. First, it is not

certain that the woman on the left holds a baby.
The object could be a jar. Second, the position of
the second woman suggests that she is an
attendant and not a rival. The scene depicted
here must represent a woman humbly making
some offering to the elderly king.

This sheet, which was unknown until its
recent appearance in the sale room, is
comparable to a number of late Rembrandt
drawings; in particular, *Issac and Rebecca Spied
upon by Abimelach,* in a private collection in
New York (Benesch, no. 988). This has been
variously dated in the late 1650s or early 1660s
(for a discussion of this drawing, which favors
the latter dating, see *Rembrandt Drawings from
American Collections,* Pierpont Morgan Library,
New York, and Fogg Art Museum, Cambridge,
Mass., 1960, no. 76). The delineation of the couple
in this study is notably similar to that of the two
kneeling women in the present sheet.

C.W.

184

Giovanni Battista Tiepolo 1696-1770
b. Venice   *d.* Madrid

70   *Saint Jerome in the Desert Listening to the Angels,* ca. 1730s
Pen and brown ink, brown wash, heightened with white, over black chalk 42.5 x 27.6 cm.

Collections: Pietro Monaco, engraved and published by him in 1743 in *Raccolta di centododici stampe di pitture della storia sacra* and then reissued with additional plates in 1763; Ann Payne Robertson (on loan to the Metropolitan Museum of Art, New York, then sold Sotheby & Co., London, Nov. 26, 1970 (no. 71)).

Exhibitions: Washington, D.C., National Gallery of Art, Sept. 29-Nov. 26, 1976, and Fort Worth, Kimbell Art Museum, Dec. 7, 1974-Feb. 9, 1975, *Venetian Drawings in American Collections;* Los Angeles County Museum of Art, *Old Master Drawings from American Collections,* Apr. 29-June 13, 1976; Washington, D.C., National Gallery of Art, *Master Drawings from the Collection of the National Gallery of Art and Promised Gifts,* June 1978 (no. 73).

Armand Hammer Collection Exhibitions: see pp. 17-18.
First exhibited San Francisco, 1971. Not exhibited San Diego; Los Angeles, 1974; Los Angeles, 1975; Moultrie.

Literature: *Important Old Master Drawings,* sale catalogue, Sotheby & Co., London, 1970, p. 113, no. 71, repr.; *Venetian Drawings in American Collections,* catalogue, National Gallery of Art, Washington, D.C., 1974, p. 68, no. 68; Ebria Feinblatt, *Old Master Drawings from American Collections,* catalogue, Los Angeles County Museum of Art, 1976, pp. 50-51, no. 58, repr.

This splendid work by Tiepolo belongs to a group of finished drawings that the artist probably intended for sale. Other drawings of a similar type are in the Museo Civico, Bassano; Civico Museo di Storia ed Arte, Trieste; the Art Institute of Chicago; the Cleveland Museum of Art; the Städelsches Kunstinstitut, Frankfurt; and the Statens Museum for Kunst, Copenhagen.

These drawings have been placed chronologically in the 1730s and were surely executed by the end of the decade since they were engraved by Pietro Monaco by 1740. In pen and rich brown washes, the drawings are heightened with white, a feature Max Goering attributes to the influence upon Tiepolo of the French artist Louis Dorigny (1654-1742), who worked for many years in Venice and died in Verona.

Tiepolo, who must be considered one of history's most brilliant draftsmen, began his career as a *tenebroso,* working with strong effects of light and shadow to create relief and depth. The present drawing reflects this chiaroscuro treatment as well as the artist's use of continuous binding lines to define the forms, both distinctive of his early style. The free application of the wash and the heavy dark accents create a fluid, dramatic background pattern for a drawing that has the monumental quality of an altarpiece. This solidity of execution, founded in the Emilian influence upon Tiepolo's earlier work, affords the utmost contrast to the dissolving weightlessness and radiant light of his later drawings.

George Knox has proposed the name of Giovanni Raggi (1712-1792), a disciple of Tiepolo, as the author of a copy of this drawing in the Museo Correr, Venice (inv. 4596). It was illustrated by Knox in "A Group of Tiepolo Drawings Owned and Engraved by Pietro Monaco," *Master Drawings,* vol. 3 (Apr. 1966), p. 389, plate 18. Another copy was in the collection of Francis Watson in London; *see also* Linda Boyer, letter, *Master Drawings,* vol. 4 (Feb. 1966).

E.F.

Giovanni Battista Tiepolo 1696-1770

71   *The Virgin and Child Adored by Bishops, Monks, and Women,* ca. 1735.
      Pen and brown wash over black chalk 42.5 x 30.0 cm.

Collections: Prince Alexis Orloff (sold Galerie Georges Petit, Paris, Apr. 29-30, 1920 (no. 134)); W. W. Crocker, Burlingame, Calif.; Augustus Pollack, Monterey, Calif.; R. M. Light & Co., Inc., Boston, Mass.

Exhibitions: San Francisco Museum of Art, *The Opening Exhibition,* Jan.-Mar. 1935; Art Institute of Chicago, *Loan Exhibition of Paintings, Drawings and Prints by the Two Tiepolos: Giambattista and Giandomenico,* Feb. 4-Mar. 6, 1938 (no. 47); Cambridge, Mass., Fogg Art Museum, Harvard University, *Seventy Master Drawings,* Nov. 27, 1948-Jan. 6, 1949 (no. 46); Washington, D.C., National Gallery of Art, *Recent Acquisitions and Promised Gifts,* June 2-Sept. 1, 1974 (no. 70); Washington, D.C., National Gallery of Art, *Master Drawings from the Collection of the National Gallery of Art and Promised Gifts,* June 1978 (no.75).

Armand Hammer Collection Exhibitions: see pp. 17-18.
First exhibited Los Angeles, 1971-1972. Not exhibited Los Angeles, 1974; Los Angeles, 1975; Moultrie.

Literature: Otto Benesch, *Venetian Drawings of the 18th Century in America,* New York, 1947, p. 31, no. 19, plate 19; Agnes Mongan, *One Hundred Master Drawings,* Cambridge, Mass., 1949, pp. 106-7, repr.; George Knox, "The Orloff Album of Tiepolo Drawings," *Burlington Magazine,* vol. 103 (June 1961); p. 275, no. 15; Christopher White, "The Hammer Collection: Drawings," *Apollo,* vol. 95 (June 1972), p. 460, fig. 8, p. 462; *Recent Acquisitions and Promised Gifts,* catalogue, National Gallery of Art, Washington, D.C., 1974, pp. 115-16, no. 70, repr.

The subject of this drawing is not yet fully identified, although the Virgin is obviously showing favor to, recommending, or interceding for, the kneeling male figure at the left. The loose long hair and seemingly unclerical attire of this figure do not readily suggest a connection with a religious order or a relationship with a familiar saint. The object he holds in his left hand may be a small book.

The drawing comes from the well-known Orloff album, which was sold in Paris in 1920. According to George Knox, the album was assembled by a Russian dilettante, Gregory Vladimirovitch Orloff (1777-1826), who published a book on Italian painting. Later the collection was inherited by Prince Alexis Orloff. The ninety-six leaves from the album included several that were highly finished and were often referred to as presentation drawings.

Otto Benesch and Agnes Mongan have ascribed the drawing to Tiepolo's mature period since it is looser in treatment than the preceding work (*Saint Jerome in the Desert*), but the dark wash that serves to accentuate the forms is still distributed in the same highly pictorial manner as in the earlier work. The contouring by means of a firm continuous line, characteristic of the earlier style, gives way here to the broken, accented strokes and modeling by flat washes, that herald the increasingly fugitive means the artist adopted in his later drawings.

In the Hammer work, the figure of Saint John can be compared generally to the larger figure of Saint Sebastian in the Fogg Museum's drawing entitled, *The Holy Family Enthroned with Saints Sebastian, Catherine of Alexandria and Francis,* dated by Knox at about 1735. Based on this comparison, the Hammer drawing can probably be assigned the same date rather than Benesch's suggested date of about 1740.

E.F.

Jean-Antoine Watteau 1684-1721
b. Valenciennes, France   *d.* Nogent-sur-Marne, France

72   *Young Girl*
Red and black chalk 21.6 x 14.6 cm.

Collections: Phillipe Wiener, Paris; Albert Meyer (sold Paris, May 24-June 8, 1935, (no. 100));
Mrs. Jesse I. Straus, New York.

Exhibitions: London, Royal Academy of Arts, *The London Exhibition of French Art, 1200-1900*,
Jan. 4-Mar. 12, 1932 (no. 713, cat. no. 765), lent by Albert Meyer; Paris, Jean A. Seligmann Gallery,
Collection Albert Meyer, May 24-June 8, 1935 (no. 100); Washington, D.C., National Gallery of Art,
Master Drawings from the Collection of the National Gallery of Art and Promised Gifts,
June 1978 (no. 80).

Armand Hammer Collection Exhibitions: see pp. 17-18.
First exhibited Little Rock, 1970-71. Not exhibited Los Angeles, 1974; Los Angeles, 1975; Moultrie.

Literature: Edmond de Goncourt, *Catalogue raisonné de l'oeuvre peint, dessiné et gravé d'Antoine
Watteau,* Paris 1875, p. 297, no. 652; *The London Exhibition of French Art, 1200-1900*, catalogue, Royal
Academy of Arts, London, 1932, p. 350, no. 713; *Commemorative Catalogue of the Exhibition of French
Art, 1200-1900,* Royal Academy of Arts, London, January-March, 1932, Oxford, 1933, p. 163, no. 765;
Dessins de maîtres du XVIIIe siècle, collection, Albert Meyer, catalogue, Jean A. Seligmann Gallery,
Paris, 1935, no. 100; K. T. Parker and J. Mathey, *Catalogue de l'oeuvre dessiné d'Antoine Watteau,*
Paris, 1957, vol. 2. p. 312, no. 577, plate 577; *The Irma M. Straus Collection of Old Master Drawings,* sale
catalogue, Parke-Bernet Galleries, Inc., New York, October 21, 1970, no. 21, repr. in color p. 37.

Watteau had a predilection for a feminine type
that appears in nearly all of his drawings of girls
and women. The face is a full oval; the nose
slightly *retroussé* with large nostrils; the eyes
heavy-lidded, long-lashed, oval-shaped, almost
slanted; the lips full, the chin plump, and the
hair generally drawn up tightly into a knot on
the top of the head. In the Hammer portrait — a
study that has not been related to a painting —
this easily recognized type appears. The modesty
and restraint of the model's pose imply that she
was drawn from life, a strong likelihood since it
is well known that Watteau made hundreds of
figure studies which he kept in bound volumes
and drew upon as elements for his pictures.

This elegantly dressed young lady looks down,
but whether in reverie or shyness it is difficult to
determine. Watteau has drawn her face in red

chalk, touching her eyebrows lightly with black.
The red chalk has taken on the grain of the
paper, giving it a porous quality. The hair is only
briefly indicated by delicate lines, the paper itself
left to convey it. Certain of the deep red accents,
such as those on the bow of the necklace and on
the lips, suggest that the chalk was moistened.
Heavy black shading sets the figure off at the
right. Despite her youth, the girl, whom the artist
has represented with great sympathy, has an
expression of maturity.

Watteau's great friend, the Comte de Caylus,
has been credited with having engraved the girl's
head in his *Figures de différentes caractères,* no.
273. On the other hand, Parker and Mathey and
E. Dacier and Albert Vuaflart (*Jean de Julienne
et les graveurs de Watteau,* Paris, 1922) attribute
the engraving to Laurent Cars.

E.F.

Jean-Antoine Watteau 1684-1721

73 *Couple Seated on a Bank*
Red, black and white chalk 24.1 x 34.9 cm.
Inscribed, lower right, in ink: *Vataux fec.*
Inscribed, lower left, in crayon: *Watteau.*

Collections: anonymous sale, Paris, 1892 (no. 72); Lallemand (sold Paris, May 2, 1894); Léon Michel-Lévy (sold Galerie, Georges Petit, Paris, June 17-18, 1925 (no. 106)); George Blumenthal, New York; Mrs. Jesse I. Straus, New York.

Exhibitions: Paris, Galerie Georges Petit, *Collection Léon Michel-Lévy,* June 17-18, 1925 (no. 106); London, Royal Academy of Arts, *The London Exhibition of French Art, 1200-1900,* Jan. 4-Mar. 12, 1932 (no. 738), lent by George Blumenthal; Washington, D.C., National Gallery of Art, *Recent Acquisitions and Promised Gifts,* June 2-Sept. 1, 1974 (no. 71); Los Angeles County Museum of Art, *Old Master Drawings from American Collections,* Apr. 29-June 13, 1976; Washington, D.C., National Gallery of Art, *Master Drawings from the Collection of the National Gallery of Art and Promised Gifts,* June 1978 (no. 79).

Armand Hammer Collection Exhibitions: see pp. 17-18.
First exhibited Little Rock, 1970-71. Not exhibited Los Angeles, 1974; Los Angeles, 1975; Moultrie.

Literature: *Les Maîtres du dessin,* Paris, 1911, vol. 3, plate 136; K. T. Parker. *The Drawings of Antoine Watteau,* London, 1931, plate 92; *The London Exhibition of French Art, 1200-1900,* catalogue, Royal Academy of Arts, London, 1932, p. 359, no. 738; *Commemorative Catalogue of the Exhibition of French Art, 1200-1900,* Royal Academy of Arts, London, January-March 1932, Oxford, 1933, p. 165, no. 780; K. T. Parker and J. Mathey, *Catalogue de l'oeuvre dessiné d'Antoine Watteau,* Paris, 1957, vol. 2, p. 326, no. 665; *The Irma N. Straus Collection of Old Master Drawings,* sale catalogue, Parke-Bernet Galleries, Inc., New York, Oct. 21, 1970, p. 34, no. 20; Christopher White, "The Hammer Collection: Drawings," *Apollo,* vol. 95 (June 1972), p. 460, fig. 6; *Recent Acquisitions and Promised Gifts,* catalogue, National Gallery of Art, Washington, D.C., 1974, pp. 116-17, no. 71, repr.; Ebria Feinblatt, *Old Master Drawings from American Collections,* catalogue, Los Angeles County Museum of Art, 1976, pp. 132-33, no. 149, repr.

The great beauty of Watteau's best drawings stems primarily from two factors, the sensitive precision of his line and the enchanting coloristic effects created by his use of three crayons: black, red and white. These features are brilliantly embodied in this sheet. Although the preliminary figures are not shown in the positions they hold in the paintings for which they served, the artist has drawn them in a remarkable way. The arms of the young man serve as an arc to support the figure of the girl; the index finger of his left hand points directly to the nape of her neck; and the right hands of both figures rest parallel to each other on the ground. In contrast to the extreme foreshortening of the man and the sketchiness of his delineation, is the complete, detailed rendering of the girl, which adds to the visual impact of the work.

The graceful gentleman in the Hammer study appears in at least two Watteau paintings: *La Famille,* in the Rothschild Collection, engraved by Aveline (E. Dacier and Albert Vuaflart, *Jean de Julienne et les graveurs de Watteau,* Paris, 1922, no. 86); and *Assemblée Galante* (Decier and Vuaflart, no. 139).

The sitters in *La Famille* have been identified on the basis of a document of 1777, as members of the family of Jean Le Bouc-Santussan, a master goldsmith who married the daughter of the famed art dealer, E. P. Gersaint, with whom Watteau lodged for a while.

E.F.

François Boucher 1703-1770
b. Paris *d.* Paris

74 *Landscape with a Rustic Bridge,* ca. 1740
Black chalk heightened with white 20.3 x 27.3 cm.

Collections: Fernand Javcl, Paris; Charles E. Slatkin Galleries, Inc., New York; Norton Simon, Los Angeles (sold Parke-Bernet Galleries, Inc., New York, May 7, 1971 (no. 207)).

Armand Hammer Collection Exhibitions: see pp. 17-18.
First exhibited Oklahoma City, 1971. Not exhibited Los Angeles, 1974; Los Angeles, 1975; Moultrie.

Literature: *Great Drawings of All Time, French: 13th Century to 1919* (selected and edited by Ira Moscowitz, text by Agnes Mongan), New York, 1962, vol. 3, no. 696, repr.; *Property of the Norton Simon Foundation and Old Master Drawings and Paintings from the Private Collection of Norton Simon,* sale catalogue, Parke-Bernet Galleries, Inc., New York, 1971, p. 160, no. 207, repr.

Agnes Mongan assigns this drawing to about 1740 when Boucher, then designing tapestries, made frequent trips into the country en route to Beauvais and the Gobelins.

It is noteworthy that in his own time Boucher was roundly criticized by the revolutionists for his pastoral paintings — his peasants resembled disguised aristocrats and his countryside was considered romantic. But a truer note emerged in his landscape drawings. Here Boucher followed such Dutch masters as Jacob van Ruisdael, Abraham Bloemaert, and Jan van Goyen, who were among the artists whose work he collected and studied. Consequently, his landscape drawings have a tranquility and restraint that contrast with the energetic sensuousness of his figural works. On the whole, the figures in his landscape drawings are subordinated to the setting, sometimes, as in the present work, appearing as *staffage.*

Boucher is known to have based his drawing style upon that of Watteau whose work he copied and engraved. It was this influence that led him to develop his supple contouring and expressive accenting of light and dark. However, the twenty years that separated the two artists can be detected in a comparison of the older artist's straight, uninterrupted line with the undulant, rococo forms of the younger man. Yet Boucher's landscape drawings were marked by a firm lineality in which short flecks of the crayon delineated the foliage and lead white was added to create the shimmer of light in the distance.

E.F.

194

François Boucher 1703-1770

75   *Venus Reclining against a Dolphin*
     Black chalk, heightened with white 22.8 x 34.3 cm.

Collections: Charles E. Slatkin Galleries, Inc., New York; Norton Simon, Los Angeles (sold Parke-Bernet Galleries, Inc., New York, May 7, 1971 (no. 206)).

Exhibitions: Washington, D.C., National Gallery of Art, Dec. 23, 1973-Mar. 17, 1974, and Art Institute of Chicago, Apr. 1-May 20, 1974, *François Boucher in North American Collections: 100 Drawings.*

Armand Hammer Collection Exhibitions: see pp. 17-18.
First exhibited London, 1972. Not exhibited Los Angeles, 1974; Los Angeles, 1975; Moultrie.

Literature: Marcel Boux, *Inventaire du fonde français, graveurs du XVIIIe siècle,* Paris, 1949, vol. 6, p. 367, no. 88 (engraving by Demarteau); Alexandre Ananoff, *L'Oeuvre dessiné de François Boucher,* Paris, 1966, vol. 1, p. 208, no. 801a; *Property of the Norton Simon Foundation and Old Master Drawings and Paintings from the Private Collection of Norton Simon,* sale catalogue, Parke-Bernet Galleries, Inc., New York, 1971, pp. 158, no. 206, repr.; Regina Shoolman Slatkin, "Some Boucher Drawings and Related Prints," *Master Drawings,* vol. 10 (1972), pp. 276-277, plate 38; *François Boucher in North American Collections: 100 Drawings,* catalogue, National Gallery of Art, Washington, D.C., 1974.

One of the most productive painters and decorators of the rococo, François Boucher, in his youth, studied briefly under François Lemoine before entering the shop of the engraver Jean François Cars. There he learned the art of etching which he was to practice all his life. Following the death of Watteau, his patron Jean de Julienne, engaged Boucher to assist in the engraving of Watteau's work as a monument to the late artist. The more than one hundred etchings Boucher made after Watteau were influential in the formation of his drawing style, a style not always readily datable.

Among his French contemporaries, Boucher was the leader in the revival of mythological subjects and in the depiction of the female nude. He often endowed his female subjects with a degree of voluptuousness not present, as, for example, in the nonsensual, classically inspired nudes of Rubens or the more sensitive, poetic Watteau nudes.

Boucher executed about fifty drawings on the theme of Venus — "the divinity adored by the courtiers of the age of Louis XV." Several of these studies show the goddess in the familiar reclining position, as in the present work, although she is accompanied by different attributes in the other works. The dolphin with which she is seen here is the sacred fish of the Greeks and it is more often associated with water deities such as Neptune's wife, Amphitrite, or the mother of Achilles, Thetis, than with Venus.

Originally published by Alexandre Ananoff as a counterproof (a proof made by rubbing the backs of both the moistened drawing and a blank sheet placed on it), the Hammer Venus has now been shown by Regina Slatkin to be the artist's original version. She has also shown that it served as the original for several copies both in the same and in reversed direction, a lost painting, and the model for an engraving in the crayon manner by Demarteau. Rhythmically unified in form and execution, the compact, fleshy body of Venus is rendered in a particularly animated way, with flowing lines, rippling curves, and outstretched left arm, while the figure's unabashed sensuality is masterfully counterbalanced by the artist's inherent refinement and *délicatesse.*

E.F.

Jean-Baptiste Greuze 1725-1805
b. Tournus, France   *d.* Paris

76   *A Tired Woman with Two Children,* 1750-61
Pen and ink, brown wash, traces of black chalk 22.5 x 27.8 cm.

Collections: John Bryson, Oxford, until 1976; Stephen Somerville, London, until 1977.

Armand Hammer Collection Exhibitions: see pp. 17-18.
First exhibited Malibu, 1977. Not exhibited Moultrie.

This is an early work, dating from Greuze's first years in Paris (1750-61) when he was influenced by Dutch and Flemish genre painting. With the exception of the two years he spent in Italy (1755-57), this is the period when Greuze made his finest studies of everyday life. Stylistically, the Hammer drawing is very similar to several drawings by Greuze in the Graphische Sammlung Albertina, Vienna. Most similar are the *Interior with a Woman and a Girl by a Fireplace* and *The Tea.* The technique is the same in all broad areas of wash, lashed and delineated with frenetic pen line and calligraphic squiggles (see also *Savoyard with Marionettes,* Albertina, and *Family Bragging,* Musée Condé, Chantilly). The model Greuze used for the old woman, probably grandmother of the children, is the same person who appears in many of his drawings (see *Old Woman with Hands Clasped,* Louvre, of 1756, which is a study for the *Father's Curse,* Louvre). If he had decided to represent the mother in this drawing, Greuze would probably have made the woman young and beautiful.

Much of his work reflects Greuze's plebeian beginnings and his concern for the impoverished family. The theme of the weary, exhausted woman in charge of lively children is a recurring one (see *The Silence,* Buckingham Palace, dated 1759), and never more eloquently expressed than in this masterful drawing by Greuze.

M.E.

Jean-Honoré Fragonard 1732-1806
b. Grasse, France   *d.* Paris

77   *Study for "The Education of the Virgin,"* ca. 1750
Charcoal 27.8 x 21.7 cm.

Collections: Private collection, France; Private collection, New York; Wildenstein & Co., Inc., New York.

Armand Hammer Collection Exhibitions: see pp. 17-18.
First exhibited Paris, 1977. Not exhibited Moultrie.

The Hammer charcoal sketch is the first conception of the black chalk drawing now in the Musée des Beaux-Arts Rouen. The Rouen drawing is a preparatory study for the painting now in the California Palace of the Legion of Honor, San Francisco (see Georges Wildenstein, *The Paintings of Fragonard,* London, 1960, no. 19; for a reproduction of the Rouen drawing, wrongly described as a study for the unfinished painting (Wildenstein, no. 17, formerly in the collection of M. Bérard, Paris), see Louis Réau, *Fragonard,* Brussels, 1956). The Rouen study is identical to the Hammer sketch except that it is larger (50.0 x 40.0 cm.) and more detailed. There is still another drawing of this subject that shows the Virgin looking up; this is a preparatory study for the oil sketch that is in the present catalogue (for this second drawing, see sale catalogue, Galerie Charpentier, Paris, June 9-10, 1953, no. 6). These are all early works, probably executed about 1750, when Fragonard was still a pupil of Boucher. Biblical subjects were unusual for Fragonard, and this one was probably suggested by his teacher as an exercise. It could not be a more charming scene, representing as it does the young Virgin leaning against her mother's knee, learning to read from the Bible held for her by angels. (See also cat. no. 7.)

M.E.

Jean-Honoré Fragonard 1732-1806

78   *The Reading*
Brown wash, the corners rounded out 27.9 x 21.0 cm.

Collections: H. Walferdin, Paris (sold Paris, Apr. 12-16, 1880 (no. 1921)); J. P. Heseltine, London; E. H. Molyneux, Neuilly-sur-Seine; Mrs. Jesse I. Straus, New York.

Exhibitions: London, Grafton Galleries, *National Loan Exhibition in Aid of National Gallery Funds,* 1909-10 (no. 99); New York, E. Gimpel and Wildenstein & Co., Inc., *Paintings and Drawings by Fragonard,* Jan. 1914 (no. 31); Paris, Musée Carnavalet, *La Vie Parisienne au XVIIIe Siècle,* Mar. 20-Apr. 30, 1928 (no. 165); Paris Galerie Jacques Seligmann et Fils, Ancien Hôtel de Sagan, *Exposition de Dessins de Fragonard,* May 9-30, 1931 (no. 55), lent by E. H. Molyneux.

Armand Hammer Collection Exhibitions: see pp. 17-18.
First exhibited Little Rock, 1970-71. Not exhibited San Diego; Los Angeles, 1974; Los Angeles, 1975; Moultrie.

Literature: Baron Roger Portalis, *Honoré Fragonard, sa vie et son oeuvre,* Paris, 1889, p. 307; *Drawings by François Boucher, J.-H. Fragonard and Antoine Watteau in the Collection of J. P. Heseltine,* London, 1900, p. 39, no. 4 (the engraving by Jules de Goncourt was reproduced in place of the drawing); *Dessins de l'école française du XVIIIe siècle, provenant de la Collection Heseltine,* Paris, 1913, no. 32, repr.; *Catalogue of Paintings and Drawings by Fragonard,* E. Gimpel and Wildenstein & Co., Inc., New York, 1914, p. 54, no. 31; Alexandre Ananoff, *L'Oeuvre dessiné de J.-H. Fragonard, catalogue raisonné,* Paris, 1961, vol. 1, p. 55, no. 62, fig. 28; *The Irma N. Straus Collection of Old Master Drawings,* sale catalogue, Parke-Bernet Galleries, Inc., New York, Oct. 21, 1970, p. 58, no. 32 repr.

Traditionally, this drawing was thought to represent Mme Fragonard reading to her younger sister, Marguerite Gérard. Mlle Gérard, who came to live with the Fragonards after their marriage, was not only the pupil of the artist but one of his favorite models. Both women were accomplished miniaturists, and Marguerite left a fine small portrait in oil of her celebrated brother-in-law.

Like the *Visit to the Nurse* and *Grandfather's Reprimand,* this drawing was originally in the H. Walferdin Collection, which was formed in Paris during Fragonard's lifetime. Walferdin (1795-1880) was born in the same city as Diderot was and shared his admiration for Fragonard. He was a physician and occasionally a man of politics. But his true pursuits were literature and art, and he was able to acquire an exceptional group of drawings by his favorite artist.

Themes centering on letters or the exchange of confidences and similar tête-à-tête situations were popular with Fragonard's audience because they implied human drama or romance. Family scenes were rarer in his work. *The Reading* records such a mood of quiet intimacy. The two sisters sit together, one reading to the other. The younger is drawn in profile, and her full skirt occupies the foreground of the drawing. The older is seen with her back to the viewer. The heads of the two women incline toward each other as they share a mutual involvement in the book.

The whole drawing is suffused with and unified by the golden tonality of the paper. The dainty, elegant silhouette of Marguerite ranks with the happiest of Fragonard's figures in which the essential is conveyed through a minimum of details. The figures of both women are, in fact, treated more broadly here than in the wash drawing of the same subject and arrangement in the Louvre (Ananoff, vol. 1, no. 61).

E.F.

Jean-Honoré Fragonard 1732-1806

79   *Grandfather's Reprimand*
Gray-brown wash over black chalk 34.3 x 45.1 cm.

Collections: Louis Antoine-August Rohan-Chabot, Paris (sold Paris, Dec. 8, 1807 (no. 43)); Baron Vivant-Denon, Paris (sold Paris, Feb. 2, 1846 (no. 269)); H. Walferdin, Paris (sold Paris, Apr. 12-16, 1880 (no. 199)); Comte de Jaucourt, Paris; Sigismond Bardas, Paris; Georges and Florence Blumenthal (sold Galerie Georges Petit, Paris, Dec. 1-2, 1932 (no. 30)); Jacques Seligmann, Paris; Mrs. Jesse I. Straus, New York.

Exhibitions: Paris, Musée des Arts Décoratifs, Pavillon de Marsan, Louvre, *Exposition d'Oeuvres de J.-H. Fragonard,* June 7-July 10, 1921 (no. 133); Washington, D.C., National Gallery of Art, *Master Drawings from the Collection of the National Gallery of Art and Promised Gifts,* June 1978 (no. 87); Washington, D.C., National Gallery of Art, *Drawings by Fragonard in North American Collections,* Nov. 11, 1978-Jan. 21, 1979; Cambridge, Massachusetts, The Fogg Art Museum, *Drawings by Fragonard in North American Collections,* Feb. 16-Apr. 11, 1979; New York, New York, The Frick Collection, *Drawings by Fragonard in North American Collections,* Apr. 20-June 3, 1979.

Armand Hammer Collection Exhibitions: see pp. 17-18.
First exhibited Little Rock, 1970-71. Not exhibited Los Angeles, 1974; Los Angeles, 1975; Oslo; Stockholm; Moultrie.

Literature: A. N. Pérignon, *Description des objets d'art qui compose le cabinet de feu M. le Baron V. Denon; (II) tableaux, dessins et miniatures,* Paris, 1826, p. 178, no. 732; Baron Roger Portalis, *Honoré Fragonard, sa vie et son oeuvre,* Paris, 1889, p. 311; Georges Wildenstein, *Catalogue de l'Exposition d'Oeuvres de J.-H. Fragonard,* Musée des Arts Décoratifs, Paris, 1921, no. 133; *Catalogue of the Sale of the Georges and Florence Blumenthal Collection,* Galerie Georges Petit, Paris, 1932, p. 28, no. 30, plate 10; Louis Réau, *Fragonard, sa vie et son oeuvre,* Brussels, 1956, p. 206; Alexandre Ananoff, *L'Oeuvre dessiné de J.-H. Fragonard catalogue raisonné,* Paris, 1961, vol. 1, p. 46, no. 41; *The Irma N. Straus Collection of Master Drawings,* sale catalogue, Parke-Bernet Galleries, Inc., New York, Oct. 21, 1970, p. 62, no. 34, repr.; Christopher White, "The Hammer Collection: Drawings," *Apollo,* vol. 95, June 1972), p. 460.

Although chalk was the primary drawing medium of Watteau and Boucher, Fragonard, influenced by Tiepolo, revived the technique of drawing with ink and wash. When he visited Italy as a young man, Fragonard was overpowered by Michelangelo and Raphael but was able to make copies of what he, in his own words, called "second-raters like Pietro da Cortona and Giovanni Battista Tiepolo."

Of the five Hammer Fragonard drawings, the two drawings of children for which the artist's young son, Alexandre Evariste, called Fanfan, is believed to have been the inspiration, must be considered the most splendid: *The Little Preacher* and *Grandfather's Reprimand.*

The outstanding features of these two drawings are the broad, flowing brushstrokes of the darker wash and the light, which floods the compositions with a vibrating, dissolving intensity. Totally suffused and illuminated, the figures themselves, despite their vigorous, broad execution and volume, seem painted with the same airiness as the palpitating atmosphere that surrounds them. The graphic techniques of Fragonard and Tiepolo are similar. Both are loose and free, but Tiepolo's technique remained linear, while Fragonard "painted" drawings, such as those referred to here, over nebulous preliminary black chalk indications.

Roger Portalis and Georges Wildenstein indicate that this drawing has had various titles in the course of time: *La Prière au Grand-Père,* 1846; *La Prière,* 1880; *La Reprimande du Grand-Papa,* 1889; and *La Visite chez le Docteur,* 1921-1932.

E.F.

Jean-Honoré Fragonard 1732-1806

80   *The Little Preacher*
Brown wash over black chalk 34.9 x 46.7 cm.

Collections: Anonymous sale, Paris, May 31, 1790 (no. 180); M. Marmontel, Paris (sold Hôtel Drouot, Paris, Jan. 25-26, 1883 (no. 100)); Richard Lion, Paris (sold Hôtel Drouot, Paris, Apr. 3, 1886 (no. 40)); M. P. Ledoux, Paris (sold Galerie Georges Petit, Paris, Mar. 5, 1918 (no. 27)); Adrien Fauchier-Magnan, Neuilly-sur-Seine; Arthur Veil-Picard, Paris, Guiraud Brothers, Paris; Jean Straus, New York; Mrs. Jesse I. Straus, New York.

Exhibitions: Washington, D.C., National Gallery of Art, *Drawings by Fragonard in North American Collections,* Nov. 11, 1978-Jan. 21, 1979; Cambridge, Massachusetts, The Fogg Art Museum, *Drawings by Fragonard in North American Collections,* Feb. 16-Apr. 11, 1979; New York, New York, The Frick Collection, *Drawings by Fragonard in North American Collections,* Apr. 20-June 3, 1979.

Armand Hammer Collection Exhibitions: see pp. 17-18.
First exhibited Little Rock, 1970-71. Not exhibited Los Angeles, 1974; Los Angeles, 1975; Nashville; Oslo; Stockholm; Moultrie.

Literature: Baron Roger Portalis, *Honoré Fragonard, sa vie et son oeuvre,* Paris, 1889, pp. 200, 310; Edmond and Jules de Goncourt, *L'Art du XVIIIe siècle, troisième série, Fragonard,* Paris, 1882, pp. 300-301; *Catalogue des tableaux anciens et modernes, aquarelles et dessins de la vente M. P. Ledoux,* sale catalogue, Galerie Georges Petit, Paris, 1918, p. 20, no. 27; *Connaissance des arts,* Aug. 1956, repr. p. 42; Louis Réau, *Fragonard, sa vie et son oeuvre,* Brussels, 1956, p. 205, fig. 79; Alexandre Ananoff, *L'Oeuvre dessiné de J.-H. Fragonard, catalogue raisonné,* Paris, 1961, vol. 1, p. 45, no. 40, fig. 18; *The Irma N. Straus Collection of Old Master Drawings,* sale catalogue, Parke-Bernet Galleries, Inc., New York, Oct. 21, 1970, p. 56, no. 31, repr.; Christopher White, "The Hammer Collection: Drawings," *Apollo,* vol. 95 (June 1972), p. 460.

Alexandre Ananoff describes *The Little Preacher* as Fanfan, the son of Fragonard. The subject was engraved with variations by N. de Launay in 1781 as a pendant to *L'Education Fait Tout,* a drawing now in the collection of Baron E. de Rothschild (Ananoff, vol. 1, no. 11, fig. 6).

The engraving may, however, have been made from the painting of the same subject formerly in the Veil-Picard Collection (G. Wildenstein, *The Paintings of Fragonard,* London, 1960, no. 471, fig. 104) rather than from this drawing.

E.F.

Jean-Honoré Fragonard 1732-1806

81 *Visit to the Nurse*
Chinese ink wash, heightened with watercolor 30.5 x 38.1 cm.

Collections: Frédéric Villot, Paris (sold Hôtel Drouot, Paris, May 16-18, 1859 (no. 122)); E. H. Molyneux, Neuilly-sur-Seine; H. Walferdin, Paris (sold Paris, Apr. 12-16, 1880 (no. 200)); Prince A. d'Arenberg, Paris; Jacques Seligmann, Paris; Mrs. Jesse I. Straus, New York.

Exhibitions: Berlin, *Königliche Akademie der Künste, Ausstellung von Werken französischer Kunst des XVIII. Jahrhunderts,* Jan.-Mar. 1910 (no. 178); Paris, Musée Carnavalet, *La Vie Parisienne au XVIIIe Siècle,* Mar. 20-Apr. 30, 1928 (no. 166); Paris, Galerie Jacques Seligmann et Fils, Ancien Hôtel de Sagan, *Exposition de Dessins de Fragonard,* May 9-30, 1931 (no. 22).

Armand Hammer Collection Exhibitions: see pp. 17-18.
First exhibited Little Rock, 1970-71. Not exhibited San Diego; Los Angeles, 1974; Los Angeles, 1975; Moultrie.

Literature: *Catalogue de la vente M. F. Villot, dessins, miniatures et estampes,* sale catalogue , Hôtel Drouot, Paris, 1859, p. 20, no. 122; Baron Roger Portlis, "Le Collection Walferdin et ses Fragonards," *Gazette des beaux-arts,* vol. 21 (1880), p. 313; Louis Réau, *Fragonard, sa vie et son oeuvre,* Brussels, 1956, pp 81, 206; *The Irma N. Straus Collection of Old Master Drawings,* sale catalogue, Parke-Bernet Galleries, Inc., New York, Oct. 21, 1970, p. 54, no. 30, repr.

Fragonard frequently depicted the same subject in a drawing and in a painting. In some instances, the drawings were studies for the later painted work; for example, preparatory drawings are known for *The Education of the Virgin,* the oil on panel now in the Hammer collection.

Baron Roger Portalis (*Honoré Fragonard,* Paris, 1889, p. 291) lists a painting, the subject of which, like the Hammer drawing of *Visit to the Nurse,* was taken from *Miss Sara,* an English novel that had been translated into French. The *Visit to the Nurse* portrays the theme of parental affection and pride. The treatment of the subject almost suggests, or parallels, an Adoration of the Child in religious art. All the figures are assembled on the foreground plane, with the light from the upper left trained on the *paterfamilias,* who holds his infant. The graded layers of the gray washes throw the illuminated figures into brilliant relief, as though the scene were taking place on a stage.

In contrast to his celebrated works on the theme of love, the familial themes in Fragonard's oeuvre reflected eighteenth century French society's pleasure in intimate home-life. This subject was most popularly portrayed in the work of Fragonard's contemporary J. B. Greuze. Greuze strongly reflected the ideas of Rousseau and Diderot, and frequently infused moralistic and didactic precepts into his art. Fragonard's work, although mirroring the "sentimentality" of his era, was free of the social propaganda advanced by the revolutionists. It is well known that Fragonard did not fit into the new order after the French Revolution. Rather, he quickly declined in status, eventually dying in poverty and obscurity.

E.F.

Jean-Auguste Dominique Ingres 1780-1867
b. Montauban, France *d.* Paris

82 *Mrs. Charles Badham,* 1816
Pencil 26.0 x 21.0 cm.
Signed and dated, lower left: *J. Ingres, Del Roma 1816*

Collections: Charles Badham, Rome; Badham family; C. Badham Jackson, London (sold Sotheby & Co., London, Dec. 12, 1928 (no. 145), repr. in cat.); Dr. Tancred Borenius, London; Wildenstein and Co., Inc., New York, sold 1929; Mrs. Jesse I. Straus, New York.

Exhibitions: New York, Paul Rosenberg Gallery, *Loan Exhibition of Ingres in American Collections,* Apr. 7-May 6, 1961 (no. 22), p. 32, repr.; Cambridge, Mass., Fogg Art Museum, Harvard University, *Ingres Centennial Exhibition, 1867-1967, Drawings, Watercolors and Oil Sketches from American Collections,* Feb. 12-Apr. 9, 1967 (no. 37); Washington, D.C., National Gallery of Art, Jan. 23-Feb. 21, 1971, Philadelphia Museum of Art, Mar. 16-Apr. 11, 1971, and New York, Wildenstein & Co., Inc., April 24-May 23, 1971, *Ingres in Rome;* Washington, D.C., National Gallery of Art, *Recent Acquisitions and Promised Gifts,* June 2-Sept. 1, 1974 (no. 72); Washington, D.C., National Gallery of Art, *Master Drawings from the Collection of the National Gallery of Art and Promised Gifts,* June 1978 (no. 93).

Armand Hammer Collection Exhibitions: see pp. 17-18.
First exhibited Little Rock, 1970-71. Not exhibited Los Angeles, 1974; Los Angeles, 1975; Moultrie.

Literature: Morton D. Zabel, "Ingres in America," *The Arts,* vol. 16 (Feb. 1930), p. 378, repr.; Jean Cassou, "Ingres et ses contradictions," *Gazette des beaux-arts,* vol. 11 (Mar. 1934), p. 157, fig. 15; Brinsley Ford, "Ingres' Portrait Drawings of English People at Rome, 1806-1820," *Burlington Magazine,* vol. 75 (July 1939), pp. 8ff., plate III, c; Hans Naef, *Rome vue par Ingres,* Lausanne, 1960, p. 27, fig. 52; Agnes Mongan and Hans Naef, *Ingres Centennial Exhibition, 1867-1967, Drawings, Watercolors and Oil Sketches from American Collections,* catalogue, Fogg Art Museum, Harvard University, Cambridge, Mass., no. 37, repr.; *Ingres,* catalogue, Petit Palais, Paris, 1967, p. 130 (portrait of Dorothea Mackie); *Apollo,* vol. 92 (Oct. 1970), p. 128, repr.; *The Irma N. Straus Collection of Old Master Drawings,* sale catalogue, Parke-Bernet Galleries, Inc., New York, Oct. 21, 1970, p. 92, no. 49, repr; *Apollo,* vol. 93, (Jan. 1971), p. 78, repr.; Christopher White, "The Hammer Collection: Drawings," *Apollo,* vol. 95 (June 1972), p. 460, fig. 7, p. 461; *Recent Acquisitions and Promised Gifts,* catalogue, National Gallery of Art, Washington, D.C., 1974, pp. 117-118, no. 72, repr.

This drawing ranks among the most enchanting made by Ingres of English visitors to Rome in the second decade of the nineteenth century.

As in the Fogg Art Museum's double portrait of *Mrs. Vesey and Her Daughter* (Mongan and Naef, no. 36), Ingres obviously took great delight in the details of his subject's attire, from the frills of her bonnet to her conspicuously draped Roman-striped scarf. All of these details are drawn with blunt and shaded strokes that heighten the contrast with the extremely delicate stippling of the soft face and long, slender neck — a contrast further emphasized by the dark accents of the profuse curls. Ingres has drawn a beguiling image of the charming feminine overdress of the early nineteenth century.

J. Fred Cain, Jr., has drawn a comparison between this portrait and that of another English lady, Dorothea Mackie. "Although the subjects face in opposite directions, both sheets display startlingly similar compositions. In each drawing the sitter has been positioned, in what appears to be the same chair, at the head of Via Gregoriana.... Ingres indicated on the drawing of Dorothea Mackie that he made the work in April of 1816. That the portrait of Dorothea Mackie may have preceded that of Margaret Badham can be supported by the fact that the latter is shown wearing summer attire: an untied bonnet and a light Roman scarf." (*Recent Acquisitions and Promised Gifts,* p. 118).

E.F.

J. Ingres. Del. Rome. 1816.

Jean-François Millet 1814-1875
b. Gruchy, France   *d.* Barbizon, France

83   *Peasants Resting*
Pastel 42.5 x 51.4 cm.
Signed, lower right: *J. F. Millet*

Collections: Boussod, Valadon & Co., Paris; Leonard Gow, Scotland; Barbizon House, London;
L. M. Flesh, Piqua, Ohio (sold Sotheby & Co., London, July 9, 1958 (no. 101), p. 21 in cat., repr.);
Thomas Agnew & Sons, Ltd., London; Norton Simon, Los Angeles (sold Parke-Bernet Galleries, Inc.,
New York, May 5, 1971 (no. 23)).

Exhibition: Paris, Ecole Nationale des Beaux-Arts, *Exposition Millet,* 1887 (no. 96).

Armand Hammer Collection Exhibitions: see pp. 17-18.
First exhibited Oklahoma City, 1971. Not exhibited San Diego; Los Angeles, 1974; Los Angeles,
1975; Moultrie.

Literature: *Catalogue descriptif des peintures, aquarelles, pastels, dessins, rehaussés, croquis et eaux-
fortes de J. F. Millet, au profit de la souscription pour élever un monument à la memoire du maître*
(introd. Paul Mantz), Ecole Nationale des Beaux-Arts, Paris, 1887, no. 96, p. 70; *Barbizon House 1937,
an Illustrated Record,* London, 1937, no. 41, repr.; *Highly Important 19th and 20th Century Paintings,
Drawings & Sculpture from the Private Collection of Norton Simon,* sale catalogue, Parke-Bernet
Galleries, Inc., New York, 1971, p. 38, no. 23, repr. in color.

The subject is a typical one for Millet—peasants resting from their labors. In this case, the man uses a tinderbox to light his pipe, while the woman, seated on the ground, watches him. Etienne Moreau-Nélaton *(Millet, ranconté par lui-même,* Paris, 1921, vol. 3) reproduces a variant (fig. 223), which he dates 1866, and two pencil sketches (figs. 341 and 342), one of which (341) is clearly for this pastel. The work is known in French as *Le Briquet,* the tinderbox.

E.F.

Eugène Boudin 1824-1898
b. Honfleur, France   *d.* Deauville, France

84   *Beach Scene,* 1869
      Pencil and watercolor 11.7 x 24.0 cm.
      Signed and dated, lower right: *Boudin 69*
      Inscribed, lower left: *Trouville*

Armand Hammer Collection Exhibitions: see pp. 17-18.
First exhibited Memphis, 1969. Not exhibited Los Angeles, 1974; Los Angeles, 1975; Moultrie.

Boudin favored watercolor to give transparency to his compositions and to capture the evanescent light effects of the beaches at which he worked. The dark range of figures defining a lateral middleground against a light foreground and background (beach and sky) is typical of his technique. The horizontal format contributes to the diffusion of focus. This scene, like the *Beach at Trouville,* shows fashionable figures taking their ease at a popular resort.

E.F.

Camille Pissarro 1830-1903
b. Saint-Thomas, Virgin Islands   *d.* Paris

85   *Pea Harvest,* ca. 1880 (recto)   *Portrait of Georges,* ca. 1880 (verso)
Watercolor and charcoal 22.8 x 27.9 cm.   Pencil and watercolor 21.6 x 29.5 cm.
Signed, lower right: *C.P.*

Collections: M. Knoedler & Co., Inc., New York; Mrs. Henry Gerstle, New York.

Armand Hammer Collection Exhibitions: see pp. 17-18.
First exhibited Memphis, 1969. Not exhibited Oklahoma City; Los Angeles, 1974; Los Angeles, 1975; Moultrie.

Literature: *Important Drawings and Watercolors of the 19th and 20th Centuries,* sale catalogue, Parke-Bernet Galleries, Inc. New York, May 15, 1969, no. 40A, repr.

There are several Pissarro drawings and aquatints of laborers in the pea and bean fields dating from between 1880 and 1896 that are close to the Hammer collection drawing in style and content: *A Kneeling Woman,* Louvre, of 1878-81; *Two Peasant Women in a Field of Beans,* of 1891, and *Two Peasant Women Talking,* of 1896, both in the Bibliothèque Nationale, Paris. The large woman on the right in the Hammer collection drawing may well have been a study for a painting of 1880 entitled *La Mère Larcheveque* (Ludovic-Rodo Pissarro and Lionello Venturi, *Camille Pissarro, son art — son oeuvre,* Paris, 1939, no. 513). They are identical in expression and attitude; only the clothes are different.

The outlines of the figures in the *Pea Harvest* have been drawn loosely and quickly, but not effortlessly. Pissarro, unlike Degas, whom he greatly admired, was not a proficient draftsman. His method of obtaining mastery over a subject was to draw it again and again and to reuse it in engravings and paintings. In a letter of July 1883, to his son Lucien, he wrote, "For preference choose simple objects...figures seated or standing.... Lots of drawings, lots and lots, remember Degas."

It was not until 1880, well into Pissarro's career, that figures appeared prominently in his work. Until then, apart from a few portraits of himself and members of his family, his predilection for landscape dominated his paintings and drawings. As there are affinities with Corot in Pissarro's early landscapes, there are connections with Millet in his studies of peasants and workmen. Unlike Millet, however, Pissarro had no moralizing vision of rural life. And if the viewer thought he saw Christian overtones in Pissarro's work, the artist liked to remind him, "It is I who am a Hebrew and it is Millet who is biblical." Pissarro continued to make figure studies such as this one until the mid-1890s, when his subject matter again changed completely and he began what was to be the last series of his life: cityscapes of Rouen, Dieppe, and Paris.

The small, vivid sketch of a child on the verso of the sheet is a portrait of the artist's third child, Georges Henri, painted when the boy was nine years old. It was probably the first study for the oil of about 1880, *Georges* (Pissarro and Venturi, no. 528) and reveals the artist's capacity for characterization, particularly evident when the sitter was well known to him.

M.E.

Camille Pissarro 1830-1903

86   *Montmorency Road*
Pencil 23.5 x 31.4 cm.
Estate stamp, lower left: *C.P.*
Inscribed, lower right: *Montmorency Enghien*

Collection: Hall Establishment.

Armand Hammer Collection Exhibitions: see pp. 17-18.
First exhibited Memphis, 1969. Not exhibited San Diego; Los Angeles, 1974; Los Angeles, 1975; Moultrie.

After studying in Paris between 1842 and 1847, Pissarro settled there permanently in 1855 at the age of twenty-five. Greatly impressed by the landscape paintings of Corot and Courbet, he soon took a studio in the suburbs and painted at such places as Montmorency, La Rochee-Guyon, Pontoise and Louveciennes. In 1856 he made a first attempt at entering the Salon and was successful with a landscape of Montmorency (Ludovic-Rodo Pissarro and Lionello Venturi, *Camille Pissarro, son art — son oeuvre,* Paris, 1939, no. 10). The Hammer collection drawing, like much of Pissarro's early work, reveals the influence of Corot in the feathery trees, silvery light, and subtle shading. Corot had advised Pissarro to study values — the property of light that renders a color dark or pale. He said, "We don't see in the same way; you see green and I see gray and 'blond,' but this is no reason for you not to work at values; for that is the basis of everything." This pencil drawing is a study in black and white of the variations or values of light about which Corot spoke.

The composition is a typical one for Pissarro. The motifs contained here appear again and again in his early paintings and engravings. Such devices as the winding road that leads the eye to a distant view, and the object, in this case the thicket at the right, that anchors the foreground of the composition are favorite ones. The notes on color and atmosphere scattered over this sheet were intended to help the artist remember the scene when he came to paint or engrave it. In technique this drawing is extremely close to one of Pissarro's first etchings, *Field near Asnières* (L. Delteil, *Le Peintre-graveur illustré,* Paris, 1923, vol. 17, no. 3), but there is no known etching or painting after this composition.

M.E.

218

Edgar Degas 1834-1917

89   *Laundress Carrying Linen,* ca. 1888-92
     Pastel 61.0 x 92.7 cm.

Collections: Atelier Degas (sold Galerie Georges Petit, Paris, first sale, May 6-8, 1918 (no. 170)); Galerie Durand-Ruel, Paris; Henri Fèvre, Monte Carlo; Mrs. Charles R. Henschel, New York; Lillie Wulf, New York; Irving Vogel, Philadelphia; Benjamin D. Gilbert, Stamford, Conn.

Exhibition: Paris, Galerie André Weil, *Degas, Peintre du Mouvement,* June 9-30, 1939 (no. 37), repr. p. 22 in cat.

Armand Hammer Collection Exhibitions: see pp. 17-18.
First exhibited New York City, 1968. Not exhibited Los Angeles, 1974; Los Angeles, 1975; Moultrie.

Literature: *Catalogue des tableaux, pastels et dessins par Edgar Degas,* catalogue of first atelier sale, Galerie Georges Petit, Paris, 1918, p. 95, no. 170, repr.; P. A. Lemoisne, *Degas et son oeuvre,* Paris, 1947, vol. 3, p. 559, no. 961, repr.

Degas returned to laundresses as a theme intermittently throughout his career. They offered him not the social overtones one senses in Daumier's use of the same subject, but a habitual and balanced movement. His first use of the pose appearing in this pastel, which also occurs in a charcoal drawing in the Hammer collection, was in a painting of about 1877 (Lemoisne, no. 410), in which it was paired with a similar figure seen from the front.

This double pose was repeated at least three times about 1902, once with horses in the background (Lemoisne, nos. 1418, 1420, 1420 bis); at the same time, the single figure was also repeated against a background of horses (Lemoisne, no. 1419). There is, finally, an almost identical pastel probably close in date to this one (Lemoisne, no. 960). In this pastel, one sees how Degas could use a figure simultaneously to render volume and to create a flat pattern activating the entire surface of the composition.

E.F.

Edgar Degas 1834-1917

90   *Jacquet,* ca. 1878
Pastel 26.0 x 20.6 cm.
Signed, center right: *Degas*

Collections: Professor Hermann Heilbuth, Copenhagen; Bachstitz Galleries; Mrs. Jesse I. Straus, New York.

Armand Hammer Collection Exhibitions: see pp. 17-18.
First exhibited Little Rock, 1970-71. Not exhibited Los Angeles, 1974; Los Angeles, 1975; Moultrie.

Literature: *Art News,* Mar. 7, 1931, p. 5, repr.; Jean Sutherland Boggs, *Portraits by Degas,* Berkeley and Los Angeles, 1962, p. 120, as ca. 1878; *The Irma N. Straus Collection of Old Master Drawings,* sale catalogue, Parke-Bernet Galleries Inc., New York, Oct. 21, 1970, p. 94, no. 50; Christopher White, "The Hammer Collection: Drawings," *Apollo,* vol. 95 (June 1972), p. 463, fig. 10.

Degas was a master at establishing three-dimensional volume without sacrificing a sense of the surface on which he was working, in this case the bare paper. Of the subject of his drawing, Jean Sutherland Boggs notes laconically, "Know nothing of him." At the time the work entered the Straus Collection, however, *Art News* identified Jacquet as Degas' framemaker. Ms. Boggs dates the portrait at about 1878.

E.F.

Edgar Degas 1834-1917

91 *Theater Box,* 1885
Pastel 56.0 x 41.0 cm.

Collections: Atelier Degas (sold Galerie Georges Petit, Paris, second sale, Dec. 11-13, 1918 (no. 162));
Mlle Jeanne Fèvre (the artist's niece), Nice (sold Galerie Charpentier, Paris, June 12, 1934 (no. 94));
Mrs. Kay, Berkshire; Reid and LéFèvre Galleries, Glasgow and London; James Archdale, London.

Armand Hammer Collection Exhibitions: see pp. 17-18.
First exhibited Los Angeles, 1971-72. Not exhibited Los Angeles, 1974; Los Angeles, 1975; Moultrie.

Literature: *Catalogue des tableaux, pastels et dessins par Edgar Degas,* catalogue of second sale, Galerie
Georges Petit, Paris, 1918, p. 87, no. 162, repr.; *Catalogue des tableaux, aquarelles, pastels, dessins,
estampes et monotypes par Edgar Degas,* sale catalogue, Galerie Charpentier, Paris, 1934, no. 94,
plate VII, repr.; P. A. Lemoisne, *Degas et son oeuvre,* Paris, 1947, vol. 3, p. 480, no. 829, repr.; Lillian
Browse, *Degas Dancers,* New York, 1949, p. 347, no. 110, plate 110 and frontis., repr. in color;
Impressionist and Modern Drawings, Paintings and Sculpture, sale catalogue, Christie, Manson &
Woods, London, July 6, 1971, p. 49, no. 48, repr. in color.

Degas began fairly early in his career to
use foreground audience figures as foils for
more or less distant figures on stage. These
foreground figures seldom functioned as
traditional *repoussoirs,* but were used as
silhouettes to establish the plane of the
composition. Inevitably, the middleground
was dropped away and the background brought
forward by the use of intense colors, obvious
paint or pastel application, and complex
compositional arrangements, as in this picture.

Lemoisne dates this and a related composition
(Lemoisne, no. 828) to 1885, although he assigns
other similar compositions to 1878-80 (Lemoisne,
nos. 476, 577). In 1879-80, Mary Cassatt, who was
close to Degas at the time, executed several
similar pictures with the auditorium rather than
the stage as a background (see Adelyn Dohme
Breeskin, *Mary Cassatt,* Washington, D.C.,
1970, nos. 61, 62, 64, 73). There is a related
Degas lithograph.

E.F.

Mary Cassatt 1844-1926
b. Allegheny City, Pennsylvania   *d.* Mesnil-Théribus, France

92   *Reine Lefebvre and Margot,* ca. 1902
Pastel on brown paper, mounted on canvas 83.2 x 67.5 cm.
Signed, lower left: *Mary Cassatt*

Collections: Felix Doistau, Paris (sold Galerie Georges Petit, Paris, June 18-19, 1928 (no. 6)); Galerie Durand-Ruel, Paris and New York, 1929; Mrs. A. L. Adams (sold Parke-Bernet Galleries, Inc., New York, Oct. 15, 1969 (no. 16)).

Exhibition: New York, Galerie Durand-Ruel, *Mary Cassatt,* Apr. 8-20, 1929 (no. 1).

Armand Hammer Collection Exhibitions: see pp. 17-18.
First exhibited Washington, D.C., 1970. Not exhibited Columbus; Los Angeles, 1971-72; London; Dublin; Leningrad; Moscow; Kiev; Minsk; Riga; Odessa; Los Angeles, 1974; Caracas; Lima; Los Angeles, 1975; Tokyo; Kyoto; Fukuoka; Nagoya; Nashville; Mexico City; Paris; Malibu; Atlanta; Denver; Buffalo; Moultrie.

Literature: *Revue de l'art,* Nov. 1928; *Bulletin de l'art ancien et moderne,* vol. 54, Nov. 1928, p. 357, repr.; *Important Impressionist and Modern Paintings and Sculpture,* sale catalogue, Parke-Bernet Galleries, Inc., 1969, no. 16, repr. in color; Adelyn Dohme Breeskin, *Mary Cassatt, A Catalogue Raisonné of the Oils, Pastels, Watercolors and Drawings,* Washington, D.C.. 1970, p. 170, no. 430, repr.

From 1901 to 1903, Reine Lefebvre, a neighbor living in the village near Mary Cassatt's Château de Beaufresne, posed for the artist, at times along with the child, Margot. Though only sixteen and seventeen years old during this association, Reine is imbued in this painting with a quiet dignity and conveys a convincing maternal relationship with the child.

Typical of Cassatt's pastels of this period, the present work almost disguises the powerful draftsmanship that won her the admiration of Degas. The free and forceful strokes seem to activate the surface in an almost random way, but ultimately the strength of line emerges in the firm design. (See also cat. nos. 110 and 111.)

L.C.

Mary Cassatt 1844-1926

*110   *Margot Leaning against Reine's Knee*, (no. 4) ca. 1902
Pencil drawing on cream wove paper 37.5 x 26.5 cm.
Initialled in pencil, lower right: MC

Collection: H.M.P., Paris.

Armand Hammer Collection Exhibitions: see pp. 17-18.
First exhibited Washington, D.C., 1980.

Literature: Adelyn Dohme Breeskin, *Mary Cassatt, A Catalogue Raisonné of the Oils, Pastels, Watercolors and Drawings*, Washington, D.C., 1970, no. 865, repr.

The figures of Reine Lefebvre and Margot in this drawing are the same as those shown in the Hammer collection pastel (cat. no. 92). Another resolution of this theme of Reine Lefebvre and Margot is to be found at the Metropolitan Museum in New York in Cassatt's major oil painting called *Young Mother Sewing*. This drawing is the last of four sketches related to that painting and the only one in which Reine is sewing. All four, however, have Margot leaning over Reine's lap as we see her here.

In this drawing the figure of Reine is quite stationary, seated comfortably in a chair, concentrating on her sewing. In contrast, the very spontaneity of the pose of Margot is emphasized by the lack of detail of outline. One can feel that the child is so sure that her mother won't mind her suddenly leaning over her lap that she does not hesitate to do so. Two angled lines are enough to define her right elbow clearly, at mother's knee; whereas three graduated, almost horizontal lines portray her back as she leans forward. The artist's ability to establish the close relationship between mother and child most eloquently at the same time that she contrasts the settled figure of Reine with the implied action of Margot as she leans forward, results in a very spirited drawing.

A.D.B.

*Recent acquisition

Mary Cassatt 1844-1926

*111   *Smiling Margot Seated in a Ruffled Bonnet,* ca. 1902
         Pencil drawing over light sanguine sketch on cream wove paper 18.5 x 16.0 cm.
         Initialled in pencil, lower right: MC

         Collection: H.M.P., Paris.

         Armand Hammer Collection Exhibitions: see pp. 17-18.
         First exhibited Washington, D.C., 1980.

         Literature: Adelyn Dohme Breeskin, *Mary Cassatt, A Catalogue Raisonné of the Oils, Pastels,*
         Watercolors and Drawings, Washington, D.C., 1970, no. 878, repr.

This pencil and sanguine sketch of Margot is one of a group of at least eight drawings in preparation for the pastel of her leaning against Reine (no. 92 in this catalogue). Here we see Margot alone, seated on an upholstered chair, or a chaise longue. She is smiling as she looks off to her left, her hands folded in her lap. (See also cat. no. 92.)

A.D.B.

*Recent acquisition

Pierre-Auguste Renoir 1841-1919
b. Limoges, France   *d.* Cagnes, France

93   *Girlhood*
Pencil 34.0 x 28.9 cm.
Signed, lower right: *Renoir*

Collection: Mrs. William Wilson, New York.

Exhibition: Paris, Galerie Charpentier, *L'Exposition au Profit des Pauvres de la Fédération Nationale des Fils des Morts pour La France,* 1949 (no. 282 bis).

Armand Hammer Collection Exhibitions: see pp. 17-18.
First exhibited Memphis, 1969. Not exhibited San Diego; Los Angeles, 1974; Los Angeles, 1975; Moultrie.

Literature: *L'Exposition au Profit des Pauvres de la Fédération Nationale des Fils des Morts pour La France,* catalogue, Galerie Charpentier, Paris, 1949, no. 282 bis.

This drawing served Renoir as the model for his drypoint *On the Beach at Berneval* (ca. 1892), which Loys Delteil also used as the frontispiece for his catalogue of the artist's prints in volume sixteen of *Le Peintre-graveur illustré.* According to Delteil, there are three states of the print. It is the last state, after the beveling of the plate, that is reproduced in his catalogue.

The placement of the two girls is reversed in the print: they face toward the middle right. Figures of bathers have been added in the background.

When the third state of the print was sold at the G. Pochet sale in 1902, it was entitled *Aux Bains de Mer.*

E.F.

Paul Cézanne 1839-1906
b. Aix-en-Provence, France   *d.* Aix-en-Provence

94   *Study of the "Ecorché"* (recto)   *Page of Studies: The Father of the Artist* (verso)
     Pencil 15.9 x 17.8 cm.   Pencil 27.3 x 17.8 cm.

Collections: Sir Michael Sadler, Oxford; Leicester Galleries, London; Edward Le Bas, Brighton
(sold Christie, Manson & Woods, Geneva, Switzerland, Nov. 6, 1969 (no. 154)).

Exhibitions: London, Leicester Galleries, *Selection of Works from the Collection of Sir Michael Sadler,*
Jan. 1944 (no. 9); London, Royal Academy of Arts, *From a Painter's Collection* (Edward Le Bas Coll.),
Mar. 19-Apr. 28, 1963 (no. 233).

Armand Hammer Collection Exhibitions: see pp. 17-18.
First exhibited Memphis, 1969. Not exhibited San Diego; Los Angeles, 1974; Los Angeles, 1975; Moultrie.

Literature: *Impressionist and Modern Drawings, Paintings and Sculpture,* sale catalogue, Christie,
Manson & Woods, Geneva, Switzerland, 1969, no. 154, repr.; Adrien Chappuis, *The Drawings of Paul
Cézanne; a Catalogue Raisonné by A. C.,* London, 1973, vol. 1, p. 249, no. 1087 bis (recto), p. 180,
no. 662 bis (verso), vol. 2, nos. 1087 bis, 662 bis, repr.

Cézanne did a painting (Venturi, no. 709) of a
plaster cast and a series of drawings (see
Lionello Venturi *Cézanne, son art — son oeuvre,*
Paris, 1936, nos. 1317, 1453, 1586) of the same
subject. The cast was mistakenly attributed to
Michelangelo in the nineteenth century and is
called the *Ecorché.* The recto of this sheet is one
of the drawings of this series.

The verso is still more interesting. In 1866 the
young Cézanne decided to paint a portrait of his
father, now in the National Gallery of Art,
Washington, D.C. The artist and his father were
never on affectionate terms. The father
disapproved of Paul's profession and after the
elder Cézanne died, his only son paid him an
ironic compliment: "My father was a man of
genius; he left me twenty-five thousand francs."
In the drawing it is perhaps significant that the
face is left blank.

E.F. and J.W.

 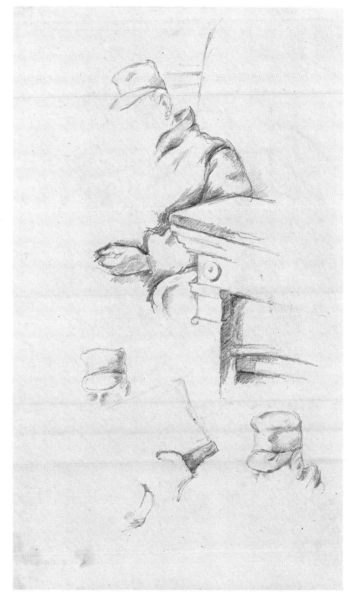

Paul Cézanne 1839-1906

95   *Mont Sainte-Victoire,* ca. 1895 (recto)   *Bedpost,* ca. 1895 (verso)
Watercolor 16.4 x 27.0 cm.   Pencil and watercolor 16.4 x 27.0 cm.

Collections: Leicester Galleries, London; Edward Le Bas, Brighton (sold Christie, Manson & Woods, Geneva, Switzerland, Nov. 6, 1969 (no. 155)).

Exhibitions: London, Royal Academy of Arts, and Edinburgh, Scottish National Gallery of Modern Art, *From a Painter's Collection* (Edward Le Bas Coll.), 1968 (no. 231).

Armand Hammer Collection Exhibitions: see pp. 17-18.
First exhibited Memphis, 1969. Not exhibited Los Angeles, 1974; Los Angeles, 1975; Moultrie.

Literature: *Impressionist and Modern Drawings, Paintings and Sculpture,* sale catalogue, Christie, Manson & Woods, Geneva, Switzerland, 1969, no. 155, repr.

The characteristic profile of Mont Sainte-Victoire, one of Cézanne's favorite motifs, is not easily discernible in this watercolor. In this work the horizontal line of trees in the middleground is emphasized. Cézanne has used wash tones close to those of the paper to increase the overall effect of the composition, an effect further enhanced by the dispersion of his accustomed broken contour.

On the verso of the sheet there is a pencil and watercolor sketch of a bedpost.

E.F.

Odilon Redon 1840-1916
b. Bordeaux, France   *d.* Paris

96   *Vase of Flowers*
Pastel 40.0 x 31.4 cm.
Signed, lower right: *Odilon Redon*

Collection: Ruth D. McVitty, Princeton, N.J.

Armand Hammer Collection Exhibitions: see pp. 17-18.
First exhibited Memphis, 1969. Not exhibited Los Angeles, 1974; Los Angeles, 1975; Moultrie.

Literature: François Daulte, "Hammer en dix chefs-d'oeuvre," *Connaissance des arts,* Sept. 1970, p. 80, repr.; Christopher White, "The Hammer Collection: Drawings," *Apollo,* vol. 95 (June 1972), p. 463.

Redon's flower pieces are at once dreamlike in their disembodiment and surreal in their clarity. With no background other than the intermediate tonality of the bare paper, the colors in this work stand out with unusual sharpness from each other and from the ground. Although the ground tends to be so infinitely atmospheric as to overwhelm the vase of flowers, the composition is wholly convincing. One hardly notices, for example, that the poppies or anemones are an unusual shade of blue.

E.F.

Paul Gauguin 1848-1903
b. Paris *d.* Fatu-Iwa, Marquesas Islands

97 *Landscape at Pont-Aven,* ca. 1888
Brush and ink 31.8 x 43.8 cm.
Inscription, lower right: *181*

Collection: Hall Establishment.

Armand Hammer Collection Exhibitions: see pp. 17-18.
First exhibited Memphis, 1969. Not exhibited Los Angeles, 1974; Los Angeles, 1975; Moultrie.

This outstanding drawing was executed during Gauguin's stay in Pont-Aven, an artists' colony on the coast of Brittany, "a land which had been little touched by Roman civilization."

According to André Schoeller, the number that appears in pencil at the lower right is an indication that the drawing was once in the possession of Emile Schuffenecker (1851-1934), an artist who was Gauguin's close friend for a time at Pont-Aven. He owned several of Gauguin's drawings, which were numbered in this fashion.

It was during his Brittany period, from 1886 to 1890, that Gauguin developed his style of Synthetism, in which he sought to extract from the forces of nature what they inherently communicated to him rather than to represent the forms of nature's outward appearance. To accomplish this end he eschewed the traditional "sciences" of painting in favor of his own subjective response and interpretation. This led to a flattening out of forms, an overriding of optical perspective, and a use of non-naturalistic color. During these years he was also influenced by the Art Nouveau movement, as is evident from the use of the curvilinear border that divides the central motif of the drawing from the one at the extreme left and gives the composition an intriguing inner ornamental frame.

It seems possible to ascribe the drawing to the period of about 1888, based on the similarity of the house and trees with those in the painting of the same name, dated 1888, now in a private collection.

E.F.

Paul Gauguin 1848-1903

98   *Parau No Te Varau Ino* (left)   *Tahitian Legend* (right)
Pen, brush, and india ink; two drawings on one sheet,
side by side 15.2 x 8.9 cm.

Collections: Galerie Druet, Paris; Sotheby & Co., London (sold Apr. 16, 1970 (no. 49)).

Armand Hammer Collection Exhibitions: see pp. 17-18.
First exhibited Washington, D.C., 1970. Not exhibited San Diego; Los Angeles, 1974; Los Angeles, 1975; Moultrie.

Literature: *Impressionist and Modern Drawings and Watercolors,* sale catalogue, Sotheby & Co., London, 1970, p. 39, no. 49, repr.

The drawing on the left is the reverse of the woodcut *Eve,* by Gauguin (Marcel Guérin, *L'Oeuvre gravé de Gauguin,* Paris, 1927, vol. 2, no. 57, repr.), and it is not improbable that it is a preliminary model for the print. The woodcut was printed in an edition of thirty. Guérin states that in the original manuscript of *Noa Noa,* Gauguin attached a photograph of a drawing representing the same figures that appear in the woodcut, but in reversed positions. The Hammer sketch may have been the one described. *Parau No Te Varau Ino* is a study for the painting of the same title, meaning "words of the devil," in the collection of the National Gallery of Art, Washington, D.C. (Georges Wildenstein, *Gauguin,* Paris, 1964, no. 458).

The support of the two Hammer studies is heavy woven J. Whatman paper. Their borders indicate that they were undoubtedly intended for prints.

E.F.

Paul Gauguin 1848-1903

99   *Tahitian Heads,* ca. 1891-93
      Page from the Tahiti sketchbook
      Pencil 16.2 x 10.2 cm.

Collections: Dr. Warner Muensterberger, New York; Robert Q. Lewis, Los Angeles.

Armand Hammer Collection Exhibitions: see pp. 17-18.
First exhibited Memphis, 1969. Not exhibited San Diego; Los Angeles, 1974; Los Angeles, 1975; Moultrie.

Literature: Bernard Dorival, ed., *Paul Gauguin, carnet de Tahiti,* Paris, 1954, no. 85; Ronald Pickvance, *Drawings of Gauguin,* London, 1970, pp. 10, 19, references to the Tahiti sketchbook; Daniel Wildenstein and Raymond Cogniat, *Paul Gauguin,* Milan, 1972, p. 88.

Gauguin's first sojourn in Tahiti lasted from April 1891 until 1893. This sheet of studies of Maori women's heads comes from the artist's Tahiti sketchbook of this period; it originally contained 130 pages, but is now broken up.

Stylistically, the Hammer drawing is remarkably close to the strong, simple, almost schematic rendering of the Gauguin self-portrait (Tahiti sketchbook, p. 5 verso) and of the head of a boy (Pickvance, *Drawings,* plate 57). The studies in the sketchbook, mostly figures and faces in silhouette, were Gauguin's way of familiarizing himself with a race of people new to him. He planned to use the sketches in his paintings when he went home. In a letter of 1892 to his wife, he wrote, "I believe that when I return, I will have in my pocket enough original material to enable me to paint for a long time." Bernard Dorival notes that nowhere in Gauguin's painting do we find faces of such intense ethnic characterization as those in this sketchbook.

M.E.

54

Paul Gauguin 1848-1903

100 *Pages from Breton Sketchbook, No. 16,* 1884-88
Page size 16.5 x 10.8 cm.

Collections: Henri Mahaut, purchased in Cherbourg before World War I; priv. coll., U.S.A.

Armand Hammer Collection Exhibitions: see pp. 17-18.
First exhibited Memphis, 1969. Not exhibited San Diego; Los Angeles, 1974; Los Angeles, 1975; Moultrie.

Literature: Henri Mahaut, "Notes synthétiques par Gauguin," *Vers et prose,* July-Sept. 1910; John Rewald, *Gauguin,* Paris, 1938, boy with a pail repr. p. 8, boy with a goose repr. p. 9; *Paul Gauguin: A Sketchbook,* facsimile ed., texts by Raymond Cogniat and John Rewald, New York (Hammer Galleries), 1962; Merete Bodelsen, *Gauguin's Ceramics,* Copenhagen, 1964, pp. 23, 38, 42, 46, 50, 87, 170, 190-91, 199-200 (Appendix A), 204, figs. 12, 13, 17, 23-25, 28-30, 40a, 110, 143 a-h, 145; Georges Boudaille, *Gauguin,* London, 1964, p. 54; Georges Wildenstein, *Gauguin,* Paris, 1964, references to the Breton sketchbook in nos. 136, 138, 139, 144, 193, 196, 201, 203, 206, 215, 216, 245, 250, 255, 256, 258, 264, 269, 282, 305; Ronald Pickvance, *Drawings of Gauguin,* London, 1970, pp. 9, 11; Mark Roskill, *Van Gogh, Gauguin and French Painting of the 1880s: A Catalogue Raisonné of Key Works,* Ann Arbor, Mich., 1970, pp. 121, 127, 140-41; Daniel Wildenstein and Raymond Cogniat, *Paul Gauguin,* Milan, 1972, p. 84, illustrating eight pages of the sketchbook; Christopher White, "The Hammer Collection: Drawings," *Apollo,* vol. 95 (June 1972), pp. 460, 463; Pierre Leprohon, *Paul Gauguin,* Paris, 1975, pp. 348-49.

With the exception of a sketchbook filled mostly with portraits, now dispersed, and an unpublished sketchbook of 1870-80 in the Nationalmuseum, Stockholm, Gauguin's Breton sketchbook of 1884-88, in the Hammer collection, contains the earliest of Gauguin's drawings. Using the figure and animal studies etched on Gauguin's ceramics as evidence, Merete Bodelsen has recently shown that all the Breton sketches in the notebook date from 1886 (the year of Gauguin's first stay in Brittany). Many of them were used, however, in paintings of 1888 (see Cogniat and Rewald, *Paul Gauguin*). During the four years the sketchbook spans, Gauguin also went to Copenhagen, Arles and Martinique, but only a few sketches remain from those visits and none from the artist's sojourn in the Caribbean.

Like most sketches, these drawings give an opportunity to see the artist's initial reaction to and first rendering of a subject. They are intimate, quick, and random impressions showing the origin of ideas that would later be developed in paintings and ceramics.

Brittany was the earliest source of Gauguin's artistic inspiration. In a letter of February, 1888, from Pont-Aven, to his old friend Emile Schuffenecker, he wrote: "I love Brittany, I find a primitive savagery here. When my wooden shoes echo on this stony ground, I hear the sound of dull, muffled power, and it is that for which I search in my painting." As one of the first expressions of Gauguin's artistic genius, the importance of this sketchbook can hardly be exaggerated.

M.E.

100 - A. *Breton Peasant*
Pencil and crayon

100 - B. *Little Breton Boy*
Pencil and crayon

100 - C. *The Bridge at Pont-Aven* (?)
Pencil and crayon

100 - D. *Two Breton Women*
Pencil and crayon

100 - E. *Head and Hand of a Monkey*
Pencil and crayon

100 - F. *Little Breton Boy with a Pail*
Pencil and crayon

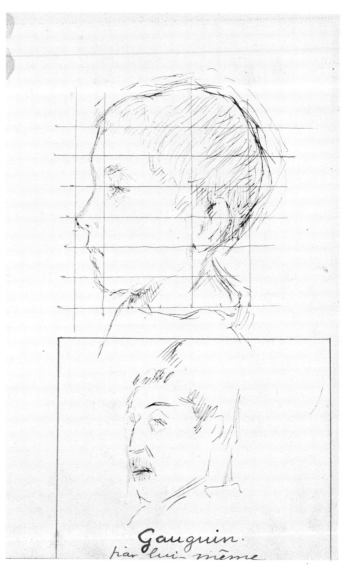

100 - G. *Landscape*
Ink

100 - H. *Head of a Child and Self-Portrait*
Ink

The head of the child has been squared for transfer to a canvas or larger paper. There is no known painting of this subject. The self-portrait is inscribed: *Gauguin par lui-même.*

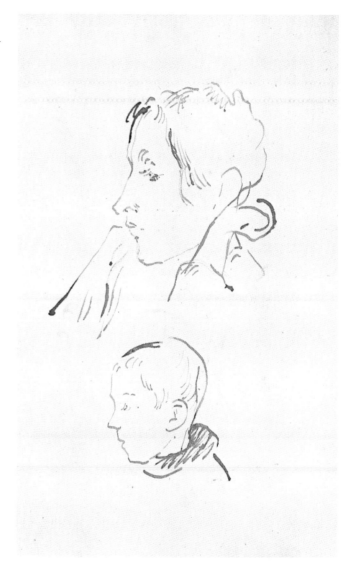

100 - I. *Head of a Child and Head of a Man*
(probably a self-portrait)
Ink

100 - J. *Profile of a Woman* and *Profile of a Boy*
Ink

Vincent van Gogh 1853-1890
b. Zundert, Holland   *d.* Auvers-sur-Oise, France

101   *The Magrot House, Cuesmes,* ca. 1879-80
Charcoal 22.9 x 29.8 cm.
Signed, lower left: *V.G.*

Collections: Charles Decrucq, Cuesmes; M. G. Delsaut, Cuesmes; Samuel Delsaut, Cuesmes (sold Christie, Manson & Woods, London, Apr. 14, 1970 (no. 41)).

Exhibitions: Paris, Musée Jacquemart-André, *Vincent van Gogh,* Feb.-Mar. 1960 (no. 199), p. 56 in cat.; Cuesmes (Borinage), Belgium, *Vincent van Gogh,* Oct. 1-20, 1960 (no. 9).

Armand Hammer Collection Exhibitions: see pp. 17-18.
First exhibited Kansas City, 1970. Not exhibited San Diego; Los Angeles, 1974; Los Angeles, 1975; Moultrie.

Literature: *The Letters of Vincent van Gogh to His Brother, 1872-1886,* London, Boston, and New York, 1927, vol. 1, Letter 136, pp. 220-25; *Museum Journal* (Stedelijk Museum, Amsterdam), ser. 5, no. 4, Oct. 1959, pp. 80-81, repr.; M. E. Tralbaut, *Le Mal Aimé,* Lausanne, 1969, p. 63; J. B. de la Faille, *The Works of Vincent van Gogh: His Paintings and Drawings,* Amsterdam, London, and New York, 1970, p. 609, no. 32, repr.; *Impressionist and Modern Drawings, Paintings and Sculpture,* sale catalogue, Christie, Manson & Woods, London, 1970, p. 34, no. 41, repr.

When van Gogh's desire to be an evangelist was frustrated by the refusal of the Committee of Evangelization to give him a permanent post, he decided to stay in the Borinage, the mining district of Belgium, at his own expense. He lived during the summer of 1880 in the home of a miner, Charles Decrucq, at Cuesmes. The drawings of the Magrot House and the Zandemennik House were once owned by Decrucq and were probably given to him as partial payment for lodgings.

Van Gogh was always desperately poor. He shared a small room with two of the Decrucq offspring, and, as he wrote his brother Theo, there were two beds, "one for the children and one for me." He continued in the same letter of September 24, 1880, "I do not want to upset the people in their household arrangement, and they have told me already that I could by no means have the other room in the house, even if I paid more, for the woman needs it for her washing, which in the house of a miner has to be done almost every day. So I would just like to take a little miner's house that costs about fr. 9 a month."

In spite of his discomfort, he was hard at work. His letter to Theo was encouraging: "Though every day difficulties come up, and new ones will present themselves, I cannot tell you how happy I am to have taken up drawing again. I have been thinking of it for a long time, but I have always considered the thing impossible and beyond my reach. But now though I feel my weakness and my painful dependency in many things, I have recovered my mental balance, and day by day my energy increases....The thing for me is to learn to draw well, to be master of my pencil or my crayon or my brush; this gained, I will make good things anywhere, and the Borinage is just as picturesque as old Venice, as Arabia, as Brittany, Normandy, Picardy or Brie."

J.W.

Vincent van Gogh 1853-1890

102 *The Zandemennik House,* ca. 1879-80
Charcoal 22.9 x 29.8 cm.
Signed, lower right: *V.G.*

Collections: Charles Decrucq, Cuesmes; M. G. Delsaut, Cuesmes; Samuel Delsaut; Cuesmes (sold Christie, Manson & Woods, London, Apr. 14, 1970 (no. 42)).

Exhibitions: Paris, Musée Jacquemart-André, *Vincent van Gogh,* Feb.-Mar. 1960 (no. 200), p. 56 in cat.; Cuesmes (Borinage), Belgium, *Vincent van Gogh,* Oct. 1-20, 1960 (no. 8).

Armand Hammer Collection Exhibitions: see pp. 17-18.
First exhibited Kansas City, 1970. Not exhibited San Diego; Los Angeles, 1974; Los Angeles, 1975; Moultrie.

Literature: *The Letters of Vincent van Gogh to His Brother, 1872-1886,* London, Boston, and New York, 1927, vol. 1, Letter 137, pp. 225-428; *Museum Journaal,* (Stedelijk Museum, Amsterdam), ser. 5, no. 4, Oct. 1959, pp. 80-81, repr.; M. E. Tralbaut, *Le Mal Aimé,* Lausanne, 1969, p. 63; J. B. de la Faille, *The Works of Vincent van Gogh: His Paintings and Drawings,* Amsterdam, London, and New York, 1970, p. 609, no. 33, repr.; *Impressionist and Modern Drawings, Paintings and Sculpture,* sale catalogue, Christie, Manson & Woods, London, 1970, p. 34, no. 42, repr.

The drawings van Gogh made in 1879-80 of the humble houses of the Borinage mining district of Belgium show the type of dwelling he hoped to rent or at least to board in. It is startling to realize that these little sheets of paper, rapidly drawn on in charcoal by the young painter and handed down from one generation to another in the Decrucq family, brought at auction, ninety years later, enough to buy all the houses in the village of Cuesmes. Yet Vincent was unable to find even nine francs a month to live in one of them!

When nothing came of his plan to find a suitable place in Cuesmes, he left the Borinage and went to Brussels. In a letter of October 15, 1880 to his brother Theo, he explained, "I thought it better to change my domicile for the present. And that for more than one reason. In the first place it was urgently necessary, because the little room where I was lodged, and which you saw last year, was so narrow, and the light there was so bad, that it was very inconvenient to draw.... It is true that nevertheless I drew there

'Les Exercices, au Fusain' and 'Les Modèles d'après la bosse de Barque,' either in the little room or outside in the garden, but now that I am as far as the portraits after Holbein in the third part of the 'Cours de Dessin,' it became impossible."

While Vincent was staying with Decrucq, Theo had written him asking his opinion of Charles Meryon. He replied, "I know his etchings a little. Would you like to see a curious thing? Put one of his correct and masterly drawings side by side with some print by Viollet-le-Duc, or some other architect. Then you will see Meryon in his full strength, because the other etching will serve to set off his work or to form a contrast. Well, what do you see then? This Meryon, even when he draws bricks, or granite, or iron bars, or a railing of a bridge, puts in his etchings, something of the human soul, moved by I do not know what inward sorrow." Van Gogh's sketches of miners' houses are likewise endowed with a soul, and there is also something in their stark bleakness that suggests van Gogh's own inward sorrow.

J.W.

Vincent van Gogh 1853-1890

103   *Old Man Carrying a Bucket,* 1882
Pencil, heightened with gray and black wash 47.6 x 21.0 cm.

Collections: Ubbergen, the Netherlands; H. S. Stork, Vienna; W. P. Maclaine Pont, Bilthoven;
Mrs. A. W. Maclaine Pont-Stork, Zwolle; J. Donna, The Hague.

Armand Hammer Collection Exhibitions: see pp. 17-18.
First exhibited Columbus, 1970. Not exhibited San Diego; Los Angeles, 1974; Los Angeles, 1975; Moultrie.

Literature: *The Letters of Vincent van Gogh to His Brother, 1872-1886,* London, Boston and New York,
1927, vol. 2, Letter 251, pp. 40-46; J. B. de la Faille, *L'Oeuvre de Vincent van Gogh, catalogue raisonné,*
Paris and Brussels, 1928, vol. 3, p. 33, no. 964, vol. 4, plate XXXV; Dr. Walther Vanbeselaere,
De Hollandsche Periode (1880-1885) in Het Werk van Vincent van Gogh, Antwerp, 1937, pp. 97, 170, 208,
409; *The Complete Letters of Vincent van Gogh* (ed. Mrs. J. van Gogh-Bonger, preface Vincent W.
van Gogh), London, 1958, vol. 1, Letter 251, pp. 504-8; J. B. de la Faille, *The Works of Vincent van Gogh:
His Paintings and Drawings,* Amsterdam, London and New York, 1970, pp. 360, 648, no. F964, repr.;
Impressionist and Modern Watercolours, Drawings and Bronzes, sale catalogue, Sotheby & Co., London,
July 2, 1970, p. 35, no. 20, repr., and on cat. cover.

In 1881 van Gogh fell in love with a widowed cousin. His passions were always violent, and when she rejected him, he was in despair. It seemed no longer possible to remain with his parents at the vicarage at Etten, and he moved to The Hague. There, in January, 1882, he met a poor, neglected prostitute, the mother of two children and again pregnant. He took her to live with him, partly from pity and partly from loneliness. The ménage was a disaster, and the painter passed through two of the most unhappy years of his life.

Art, however, was a solace, and he drew constantly. In an undated letter to his brother Theo (no. 251), he wrote, "You have received my letter in which I wrote you how during my work the idea developed itself of making figures *from the people for the people.* How it seemed to me that it would be a good thing, not commercially, but of charity and duty if a few persons combined to do it...I have said to myself that the duty that comes first to me is to try my very best on the drawings. So that since my last letter on the subject I have now made a few new ones. In the first place, a Sower....Then one of those little old fellows in short jacket and high old top-hat, which one meets sometimes in the dunes. He carries home a basketful of peat....These fellows are all in action and that fact especially must be kept in mind in the choice of subjects, I think. You know yourself how beautiful are the numerous figures in rest which are made so very, very often. They are made more often than figures in action. It is always very tempting to draw a figure at rest; to express action is very difficult, and the former effect is in many people's eyes more 'pleasant' than anything else. But this 'pleasant' aspect may not take from the truth, and the truth is that there is more drudgery than rest in life. So you see my idea about it all is especially this, that I for my part, try to work for the truth."

J.W.

Vincent van Gogh 1853-1890

104 *Man Polishing a Boot,* 1882
Black chalk, pencil, heightened with white and gray wash 48.3 x 26.7 cm.

Collections: H. P. Bremmer, The Hague; Heirs of H. P. Bremmer, The Hague; E. J. van Wisselingh & Co., Amsterdam; Mrs. J. G. ter Kuile-ter Kuile, Switzerland (sold Christie, Manson & Woods (New York), Houston, Apr. 6, 1970 (no. 61)).

Exhibition: Amsterdam, E. J. van Wisselingh & Co., *Vincent van Gogh, Aquarelles et Dessins de l'Epoque 1881-1885, provenant de collections particulières néerlandaises,* Apr. 19-May 18, 1961 (no. 19), repr. in cat.

Armand Hammer Collection Exhibitions: see pp. 17-18.
First exhibited Kansas City, 1970. Not exhibited San Diego; Los Angeles, 1974; Los Angeles, 1975; Moultrie.

Literature: *The Letters of Vincent van Gogh to His Brother, 1872-1886,* London, Boston, and New York, 1927, vol. 1, Letter 235, pp. 530-33, Letter 236, pp. 533-35, Letter 238, pp. 539-43; J. B. de la Faille, *L'Oeuvre de Vincent van Gogh, catalogue raisonné,* Paris and Brussels, 1928, vol. 3, no. 969, vol. 4, plate XXXVII; Dr. Walther Vanbeselaere, *Der Hollandsche Periode (1880-1885) in Het Werk van Vincent van Gogh,* Antwerp, 1937, pp. 88, 91, 170, 190, 409; *Letters to an Artist: From Vincent van Gogh to Anton Ridder van Rappard, 1881-1885* (trans. Rela van Messel, introd. Walter Pach), New York, 1937, p. 48; *The Complete Letters of Vincent van Gogh* (ed. Mrs. J. van Gogh-Bonger, preface Vincent W. van Gogh), London, 1958, vol. 1, Letter 235, pp. 463-66, Letter 236, pp. 466-67, Letter 238, pp. 470-73; J. B. de la Faille, *The Works of Vincent van Gogh: His Paintings and Drawings,* Amsterdam, London, and New York, 1970, pp. 361, 648, no. F969, repr. p. 361; *Impressionist, American and Modern Paintings and Watercolors,* sale catalogue, Christie, Manson & Woods (New York), Houston, 1970, no. 61, p. 46, repr.

Van Gogh wrote his brother Theo in an undated letter (no. 235), "Once again being engrossed in drawing, I sometimes think there is nothing so delightful as drawing.... I was interrupted in writing this letter by the arrival of my model. And I worked with him until dark. He wears a large old overcoat, which gives him a curious broad figure."

Perhaps the reference in this letter was to the model in the Hammer drawing, who patiently brushes a worn-out boot. Van Gogh's studies of old men are drawn with compassion and understanding. As he remarked to his brother (Letter no. 239), "I believe that if one wants to make figures one must have a warm feeling, what *Punch* calls in his Christmas pictures: Goodwill to all — that means one must have real love for one's fellow creatures."

Love for one's fellow creatures imbues every line of the Hammer drawing. There is an innate dignity in the old veteran who humbly cleans a shoe. He was probably once a soldier, since in his lapel there is a medal in the form of a Maltese cross. He is now apparently poor and earns a pittance posing for a still poorer artist, an artist who must cadge a little money from his brother to whom he wrote (Letter no. 238), "Drawing much after the model... is rather expensive, but it fills my portfolios in proportion as it empties my purse."

Vincent's portfolios were bursting with drawings. In another letter (no. 239), he told Theo, "When I happened to arrange my drawings this morning, namely the studies after the model made since your last visit (not counting the older studies or those I drew in my sketchbook), I counted about a hundred....I do not know whether all painters, even those who look down on my work to such a degree that they think it below themselves to take the least notice of it, work more than I do."

It was this painstaking apprenticeship that gave van Gogh mastery and made him one of the greatest draftsmen of the nineteenth century.

J.W.

Georges Seurat 1859-1891
b. Paris   *d.* Paris

105   *Study after "The Models,"* 1888
Pen and ink 26.0 x 16.5 cm.
Signed, lower left: *Seurat*

Collections: Emile Seurat, Paris; Alexandre Natanson, Paris; Galerie Bolette Natanson, Paris; Jean-Charles Moreux, Paris; Mme Jean-Charles Moreux, Paris; Wildenstein & Co., Inc., New York; Norton Simon, Los Angeles (sold Parke-Bernet Galleries, Inc., New York, May 5, 1971 (no. 46)).

Exhibitions: Paris, La Revue Blanche, *Seurat,* Mar. 19-Apr. 5, 1900 (hors cat.); Paris, Galerie Bernheim-Jeune, *Rétrospective Georges Seurat,* Dec. 14, 1908-Jan. 9, 1909 (no. 197); Paris, Galerie Bernheim-Jeune, *Les Dessins de Seurat,* Nov. 29-Dec. 24, 1926 (no. 114); London, Galerie Syrie Maugham, Bolette Natanson, *Seurat,* May 21-June 7, 1935; Paris, Galerie Paul Rosenberg, *Georges Seurat,* Feb. 3-29, 1936 (no. 130), suppl.; Paris, Galerie Bolette Natanson, "Les Cadres," *Peintres de la Revue Blanche,* 1936 (no. 50), suppl.; Paris, Musée Jacquemart-André, *Seurat,* Nov.-Dec. 1957 (no. 55); Washington, D.C., National Gallery of Art, *Recent Acquisitions and Promised Gifts,* June 2-Sept. 1, 1974 (no. 73).

Armand Hammer Collection Exhibitions: see pp. 17-18.
First exhibited Oklahoma City, 1971. Not exhibited San Diego; Los Angeles, 1974; Los Angeles, 1975; Moultrie.

Literature: Paul Adam, "Les Impressionistes à l'Exposition des Indépendants," *La Vie moderne,* Apr. 15, 1888, p. 229, repr.; André Lhote, *Georges Seurat,* Rome, 1922, p. II, repr.; Florent Fels, "Les Dessins de Georges Seurat," *L'Amour de l'art,* no. 1, Jan. 1927, p. 43, repr.; Gustave Kahn, *Les Dessins de Georges Seurat,* Paris, 1928, vol. 2, plate 98; Waldemar George, *Seurat et le divisionnisme,* Paris, 1928, p. 15, repr.; Thadée Natanson, "Sur une exposition des peintres de la Revue Blanche," *Arts et métiers graphiques,* no. 54, Aug. 15, 1936, p. 16, repr.; Robert J. Goldwater, "Some Aspects of the Development of Seurat's Style," *Art Bulletin,* vol. 23, no. 2 (June 1941), pp. 117-30, fig. 4; Henri Dorra and John Rewald, *Seurat, l'oeuvre peint, biographie et catalogue critique,* Paris, 1959, p. 222, no. 179a, repr.; C. M. de Hauke, *Seurat et son oeuvre,* Paris, 1961, vol. 2, p. 254, no. 665, repr.; *Highly Important 19th and 20th Century Paintings, Drawings and Sculpture from the Private Collection of Norton Simon,* sale catalogue, Parke-Bernet Galleries, Inc., New York, 1971, p. 88, no. 46, repr.; A. Chastel, *Seurat,* Milan, 1972, pp. 105-6, no. D47, repr.; L. Hautecoeur, *Georges Seurat,* Milan, 1972, pp. 42-43, plate 2; *Recent Acquisitions and Promised Gifts,* catalogue, National Gallery of Art, Washington, D.C., 1974, pp. 118-19, no. 73, repr.

Despite the brevity of Seurat's career, a prodigious body of drawings celebrates his genius as a draftsman. Curiously, among the several hundred drawings assigned to his hand, only two were intended by the artist to be graphically reproduced. The present drawing derives from one of Seurat's major canvases, *The Models,* and was used for an illustration in the April 15, 1888, issue of *La Vie moderne* (see Dorra and Rewald, *Seurat*). In the following year, Seurat designed a cover for *L'Homme à femme,* a novel by the Polish writer Victor Joze. Both of these studies were in pen and ink, a technique Seurat rarely used for his drawings. Another atypical feature common to both is the undisguised use of outline.

J.F.C.

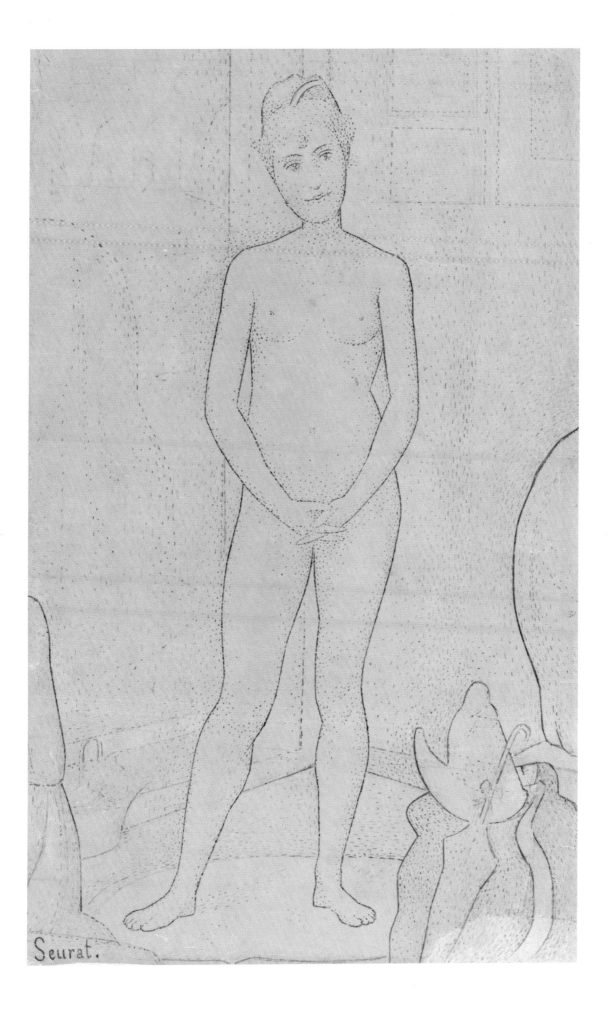

Seurat.

Henri-Edmond Cross 1856-1910
b. Douai, France *d.* Lavandou, France

106 *Cypresses,* 1896
Gouache 24.1 x 33.7 cm.

Collections: William J. Holliday, Indianapolis; Modern Art Foundation, Geneva, Ill.; Pierre Matisse Gallery, New York.

Exhibition: Cleveland Museum of Art, *Tenth Exhibition of Watercolors and Pastels,*
Jan. 10-Feb. 12, 1933.

Armand Hammer Collection Exhibitions: see pp. 17-18.
First exhibited Memphis, 1969. Not exhibited San Diego; Los Angeles, 1974; Los Angeles, 1975; Moultrie.

Literature: Isabelle Compin, *H. E. Cross,* Paris, 1964, repr. pp. 146, 338.

In her publication *H.E. Cross,* Isabelle Compin reproduces an oil (64.7 x 92.0 cm.) painted in 1896 entitled *Nocturne* that depicts an image identical to the one shown here. She also reproduces a four-color lithograph, 28.2 x 40.9 cm., published by Ambroise Vollard in 1896 as *La Promenade.* Compin believes she may have found the source of the subject in a play of 1892 by Edouard Dujardin. In the play, night is falling, and the four Floramyes, preparing to leave the isle of Antonia, lament: "Adieu, les rives où nous avons vécu! Adieu, les charmants bords où nos songes longtemps ne sont plus!"
(*Le Chevalier Passé,* Act III, Scene I)

E.F.

Pierre Bonnard 1867-1947
b. Fontenay-aux-Roses, France *d.* Cannet, France

107 *Girl Putting on Her Stocking*
(Also known as *Girl Drying Her Knees*)
Pencil 33.0 x 24.1 cm.
Signed, lower right: *Bonnard*

Collection: Norton Simon, Los Angeles (sold Parke-Bernet Galleries, Inc., New York, May 5, 1971).

Armand Hammer Collection Exhibitions: see pp. 17-18.
First exhibited Memphis, 1969. Not exhibited San Diego; Los Angeles, 1974; Los Angeles, 1975; Moultrie.

Literature: Denys Sutton, *Catalogue of the Bonnard Exhibition,* Royal Academy of Arts, London, winter, 1966; André Fermigier, *Bonnard,* London, 1970, p. 33, repr.; Jean and Henry Dauberville, *Bonnard — catalogue raisonné,* Paris, 1973.

Bonnard was fascinated by the ancient theme of the bath, a subject he first painted in 1895 and continued to depict until 1938. Like most artists, he wished to paint from the nude. The privacy of the bathroom and the boudoir made a relaxed and natural setting in which to portray this figure. Bonnard met his wife, Maria Boursin, known as Marthe de Méligny, in 1894. Apparently, she had a passion for bathing, and it is she who figures in most of Bonnard's paintings and drawings of this subject. As early as 1886, Bonnard had been impressed by the nude studies he had seen exhibited by Degas at the Durand-Ruel Gallery. Though he did not treat the nude figure in the same sculptural way as Degas treated it, Bonnard did study Degas' rendering of the effect of atmosphere and light on the naked body. The figure in the Hammer drawing is placed in an empty space with the surroundings indicated by the curtain and the outline of the bathtub. Such a simplification of the background occurs in Bonnard's work after 1900 (see Denys Sutton, *Catalogue of the Bonnard Exhibition*). The Hammer drawing has been executed with quick, repetitious hatching technique characteristic of Bonnard's drawings of the 1920s. A pencil study, called *La Toilette* and similiar in size (33.0 x 21.8 cm.), was probably made at the same time as the present drawing. It is handled as the Hammer drawing is, though with a heavier pencil, and a slightly different pose (Fermigier, repr. p. 33, as Bonnard about 1920, whereabouts unknown). Four paintings of a young woman after the bath are related to the Hammer sketch and all date from between 1924 and 1927 (Dauberville, nos. 1277, 1278, 1283, and 1388).

M.E.

Pablo Picasso 1881-1973
b. Malaga, Spain   *d.* Mougins, France

108   *Female Nude,* ca. 1906 (recto)   *Young Man,* ca. 1906 (verso)
      Pencil 16.5 x 10.2 cm.   Pen and ink 16.5 x 10.2 cm.
      Signed, upper right: *Picasso*   Signed, lower right: *Picasso*

Collections: Saidenberg Gallery, New York; George Axelrod, New York.

Armand Hammer Collection Exhibitions: see pp. 17-18.
First exhibited Kansas City, 1970. Not exhibited San Diego; Los Angeles, 1974; Los Angeles,
1975; Moultrie.

Literature: *Impressionist and Modern Drawings and Watercolors,* sale catalogue, Sotheby & Co.,
London, Apr. 16, 1970, pp. 118-19, no. 92, repr.

This double-sided drawing belongs to the period of 1906, and the female nude incorporates many of the "classicizing" features Picasso adopted at that time when his work became simplified, more abstract and sculptural. The face with its distant gaze is delineated with a minimum of lines and accords with various other "masklike" portraits of the period. But the relatively broad, squat body, treated in summary fashion, possesses the quality of the late Iberian sculpture that influenced Picasso's earlier work.

That the verso sketch is so close to a caricature suggests that it may have been drawn of a friend, perhaps at a cafe. An earlier sketch of roughly the same type, in which the man leans his arm on a cafe table, was formerly in the Galerie Rosengart in Lucerne, Switzerland.

C.M.

Andrew Wyeth
b. Chadds Ford, Pennsylvania 1917

109   *Brandywine Valley,* 1940
Watercolor 53.3 x 73.7 cm.
Signed and dated, lower right: *Andrew Wyeth 1940*

Collection: Private collection (sold, Christie, Manson & Woods (New York), Houston, Apr. 6, 1970 (no. 21)).

Literature: *Impressionist, American and Modern Paintings and Watercolors*, sale catalogue, Christie, Manson & Woods (New York), Houston, 1970, no. 21, p. 19, repr.

Armand Hammer Collection Exhibitions: see pp. 17-18.
First exhibited Washington, D.C., 1970. Not exhibited San Diego; Los Angeles, 1974; Los Angeles, 1975; Moultrie.

The freely flowing washes of this early Wyeth work superbly utilize the transparent qualities of transparent watercolor, and contrast with the artist's more recent drybrush works, which are similiar to his tempera paintings. Wyeth developed absolute mastery of the medium at an early age through the rigorous tutelage of his father and lessons found in the work of such artists as Winslow Homer. This watercolor, painted more than forty years ago at the John Chad house in Chadds Ford, Pa., reveals Wyeth's deep involvement with the Brandywine Valley, where he still lives and works without regard for contemporary trends in the United States or abroad.

L.C.

Index

Numbers refer to page numbers.

Bernard, Emile
108 *Wheat Harvest*

Bonnard, Pierre
118 *Street Scene*
120 *Nude against the Light*
268 *Girl Putting on Her Stocking*

Boucher, François
194 *Landscape with a Rustic Bridge*
196 *Venus Reclining against a Dolphin*

Boudin, Eugène
62 *Sailing Ships in Port*
64 *Quay at Camaret*
66 *Beach at Trouville*
214 *Beach Scene*

Caillebotte, Gustave
68 *Square in Argenteuil*

Cassatt, Mary
154 *Summertime*
230 *Reine Lefebvre and Margot*
232 *Margot Leaning against Reine's Knee*
234 *Smiling Margot Seated in a Ruffled Bonnet*

Cézanne, Paul
84 *Boy Resting*
238 *Study of the "Écorché"* (recto)
238 *Page of Studies: The Father of the
       Artist* (verso)
240 *Mont Sainte-Victoire* (recto)
240 *Bedpost* (verso)

Chagall, Marc
142 *Blue Angel*

Corot, Jean Baptiste Camille
50 *Medieval Ruins*
52 *Harvester under Trees*
54 *Distant View of Mantes Cathedral*
56 *Portrait of a Girl*
58 *Morning*
60 *Pleasures of Evening*

Correggio, Antonio Allegri da
180 *Study for the "Madonna della
       Scodella"* (recto)
180 *Study for a Fresco of Saint Matthew
       and Saint Jerome* (verso)

Cross, Henri-Edmond
266 *Cypresses*

Degas, Edgar
94 *Three Dancers in Yellow Skirts*
222 *Laundresses Carrying Linen*
224 *Laundress Carrying Linen*
226 *Jacquet*
228 *Theater Box*

Derain, André
130 *Still Life with Basket, Jug and Fruit*

Dürer, Albrecht
164 *Tuft of Cowslips*

Eakins, Thomas
152 *Portrait of Sebastiano Cardinal Martinelli*

Fantin-Latour, Henri
88 *Peonies in a Blue and White Vase*
90 *Portrait of Miss Edith Crowe*
92 *Roses*

Fragonard, Jean-Honoré
44 *The Education of the Virgin*
200 *Study for "The Education of the Virgin"*
202 *The Reading*
204 *Grandfather's Reprimand*
206 *The Little Preacher*
208 *Visit to the Nurse*

Gauguin, Paul
104 *Bonjour M. Gauguin*
244 *Landscape at Pont-Aven*
246 *Parau No Te Varau Ino* (left)
246 *Tahitian Legend* (right)
248 *Tahitian Heads*
250 *Pages from Breton Sketchbook No. 16*

Géricault, Théodore
48 *Portrait of a Gentleman*

Gogh, Vincent van
110 *Garden of the Rectory at Nuenen*
112 *Lilacs*
114 *The Sower*
116 *Hospital at Saint-Rémy*
256 *The Magrot House, Cuesmes*
258 *The Zandemennik House*
260 *Old Man Carrying a Bucket*
262 *Man Polishing a Boot*

Goya y Lucientes, Francisco de
46 *El Pelele*

Greuze, Jean-Baptiste
198 *A Tired Woman with Two Children*

Harnett, William Michael
146 *Still Life*

Ingres, Jean-Auguste Dominique
210 *Mrs. Charles Badham*

Laurencin, Marie
140 *Women in the Forest*

Leonardo da Vinci
168 *Sheet of Studies*

Manet, Edouard
220 *Man Wearing a Cloak* (recto)
220 *Man Wearing a Cloak* (verso)

Michelangelo Buonarroti
170 *Male Nude* (recto)
172 *Male Nude* (verso)

Millais, Sir John Everett
106 *Caller Herrin'*

Millet, Jean-François
212 *Peasants Resting*

Modigliani, Amedeo
132 *Woman of the People*

Monet, Claude
72 *View of Bordighera*

Moreau, Gustave
98 *Salome*
102 *King David*

Morisot, Berthe
82 *Jeune Fille au Chien (Young Girl with a Dog)* Paule Gobillard — Niece of Berthe Morisot

Picasso, Pablo
270 *Female Nude* (recto)
270 *Young Man* (verso)

Pissarro, Camille
74 *Boulevard Montmartre, Mardi Gras*
216 *Pea Harvest* (recto)
216 *Portrait of Georges* (verso)
218 *Montmorency Road*

Prendergast, Maurice Brazil
156 *On the Beach*

Raphael
174 *Study for a Fresco of the Prophets Hosea and Jonah*

Redon, Odilon
242 *Vase of Flowers*

Rembrandt van Rijn
20 *Juno*
26 *Portrait of a Man Holding a Black Hat*
30 *Portrait of a Man of the Raman Family*
182 *Study of a Beggar Man and Woman*
184 *A Biblical Subject*

Remington, Frederic
158 *Cowpuncher's Lullaby*

Renoir, Pierre-Auguste
76 *Grape Pickers at Lunch*
78 *Antibes*
80 *Two Girls Reading*
236 *Girlhood*

Rouault, Georges
136 *Circus Girl*

Rubens, Peter Paul
34 *Adoration of the Shepherds*
36 *Young Woman with Curly Hair*
40 *The Israelites Gathering Manna in the Desert*

Russell, Charles Marion
160 *The War Party*

Sargent, John Singer
148 *Dr. Pozzi at Home*
150 *Portrait of Mrs. Edward L. Davis and Her Son, Livingston Davis*

Sarto, Andrea del
178 *Female Head*

Seurat, Georges
264 *Study after "The Models"*

Sisley, Alfred
70 *Timber Yard at Saint-Mammès*

Soutine, Chaim
134 *The Valet*

Stuart, Gilbert
144 *Portrait of George Washington*

Tiepolo, Giovanni Battista
186 *Saint Jerome in the Desert Listening to the Angels*
188 *The Virgin and Child Adored by Bishops, Monks and Women*

Toulouse-Lautrec, Henri de
96 *In the Salon*

Vlaminck, Maurice de
138 *Summer Bouquet*

Vuillard, Edouard
122 *In the Bus*
124 *At the Seashore*
126 *Rue Lepic, Paris*
128 *Interior*

Watteau, Jean-Antoine
190 *Young Girl*
192 *Couple Seated on a Bank*

Wyeth, Andrew
272 *Brandywine Valley*

C. P.

Edouard Manet 1832-1883
b. Paris   *d.* Paris

87   *Man Wearing a Cloak,* 1852-58 (recto)   *Man Wearing a Cloak,* 1852-58 (verso)
Charcoal 40.6 x 22.5 cm.   Charcoal 40.6 x 22.5 cm.
Signed, lower left: *ed m*

Collections: Hector Brown, London; Arcade Gallery, London; Francis Cooke, Esq., London; Matthiesen Gallery, London; Hugh Chisholm, New York.

Exhibition: Washington, D.C., National Gallery of Art, *Master Drawings from the Collection of the National Gallery of Art and Promised Gifts,* June 1978 (no. 97).

Armand Hammer Collection Exhibitions: see pp. 17-18.
First exhibited Columbus, 1970. Not exhibited San Diego; Los Angeles, 1974; Los Angeles, 1975; Moultrie.

Literature: Alain de Leiris, *The Drawings of Edouard Manet,* Berkeley and Los Angeles, 1969, no. 135 (recto), no. 136 (verso), figs. 186, 187; *Impressionist and Modern Drawings, Paintings and Sculpture,* sale catalogue, Christie, Manson & Woods, London, June 30, 1970, no. 1, repr.

These monumental studies of mantled figures were drawn under the influence of Manet's teacher, Thomas Couture, who encouraged a broad style of modeling, with large masses of light blocked out by straight and simplified linear contouring. This approach was based on the bold technique used by the Italian masters of the Renaissance in fresco painting. Manet made many drawings after Renaissance artists in order to master the elements of design and composition. However, in the present drawings the glancing surfaces of light created from the reserved parts of the paper bespeak Manet's early interest in a flattening and generalizing of the form rather than its strict structural volume.

E.F.

Edgar Degas 1834-1917
b. Paris *d*. Paris

88 *Laundresses Carrying Linen*
Charcoal 43.2 x 58.4 cm.

Collections: Atelier Degas (sold Galerie Georges Petit, Paris, fourth sale, July 2-4, 1919 (no. 357), repr. in cat.); Monsieur S —.

Armand Hammer Collection Exhibitions: see pp. 17-18.
First exhibited New Orleans, 1970. Not exhibited San Diego; Los Angeles, 1974; Los Angeles, 1975; Moultrie.

Literature: *Collections de Monsieur S —* , sale catalogue, Hôtel Drouot, Paris, Nov. 13, 1969, no. 20, plate III.

The composition of *Laundresses Carrying Linen* is a masterpiece of balanced tensions, and one of the most beautiful designs that Degas ever achieved. The thrust and counterthrust of the two women, joined in the center by their overlapping burdens, convey an effect of forces in perfect equilibrium. Note also how effectively the figures are placed on the sheet. As Ebria Feinblatt has noted in other catalogues of the Hammer collection, "The softness of much of this drawing suggests that it may be a reworked counterproof, probably executed rather late in Degas' career.

The figure at the right is almost identical to that in the Hammer *Laundress Carrying Linen,* but in reverse." The astute supposition that the drawing may be a counterproof suggests that Degas, having created a design of such brilliant originality, wished to preserve it in more than one example and that he also wanted to see how his composition would look in reverse, which the counterproof would show. However, if there was a counterpart of which this drawing is a reproduction, it has disappeared.

J.W.